Mrs. Ralph King
1811 North 82nd St
Kansas City, Kans. 66112

tele. 788-5712

Marie Walston,
the author,
is Fern Leible's Sister.

Elizabeth Anderson
very good

Betty Morgan — I really enjoyed
this book

Jack Morgan

Great memories!
terms like "the strand table"
" the blacksmith shop" and
a rounded up the cows " &
many more have made this book
a time of wonderful reflection
for me   Thank you marie &
thankyou kern & thankyou Ji
                    Richard Bryan

To Vi King

These
Were
My
Hills
❖

Best wishes
Marie Walston

These
Were
My
Hills

Marie Walston

Judson Press
valley forge

THESE WERE MY HILLS

Copyright © 1972

Judson Press, Valley Forge, Pa. 19481

Library of Congress Cataloging in Publication Data

Walston, Marie.
    These were my hills.

    I. Title.
BX6495.W3A3   286'.1'0924 B   72-189436
ISBN 0-8170-0563-3

While this book is a story of the author's personal experience, all names of persons included in the account have been changed.

Printed in the U.S.A.

Contents

I.
Getting
Acquainted
with
Uncle Ben

Some of my fondest childhood memories have to do with those years we spent in the Ozarks where my father established a Baptist church. Especially dear were those periods following supper when the dishes were put away and the family congregated on the front porch for stories of bygone days.

Uncle Ben (actually my father's sharecropper) was a Civil War baby, a second-generation Ozarker, and a perpetual source of stories. A widower, Uncle Ben had traveled "for a spell" following his wife's death. My parents were interested in the cities he had visited, and Uncle Ben knew all the prospective church members in the area. But my brother and I cared little for this grown-up talk. We would maneuver the conversation so that he got started on what Mother termed "one of his animal tales."

I knew that many of Uncle Ben's accounts concerning animal behavior were laced with superstition and hyperbole. But the textbooks that told me so couldn't begin to compete with the colorful tales he geared to my imagination.

I can see him still, rosy-faced with a fringe of white hair

encircling his shiny bald head, settling back in a cane-bottomed chair. "Well, kids," he said, "let me get a chaw of tobakker, and I'll tell you what I know of wildcats."

While he was getting settled just right, the spring sun dropped behind Woods Mountain. Out in our barn lot, Old Red, the leader of our cow herd, closed her eyes and began to pant, adding a rhythmic ding, ding, ding of her bell to the katydid-jarfly symphony already in full swing. In this peaceful setting, Uncle Ben began.

"Wildcats ain't noways what they once were. Nowadays if a body kills a cat weighing forty pounds, he thinks he has really done something. But the time was when it wasn't unusual to hear tell of a cat weighing a hundred pounds easy. Fact is, my sister Mary and I saw one that looked as though it might have weighed more.

"We were ten and twelve then. My Pa believed in chores, and our job was to see that the water buckets were filled before dark. But young'un like, sometimes we would forget. Pa kept saying he was going to send us out after dark, but we didn't think he ever would. One night Ma had to sit with a sick neighbor. When Pa came in, all tired out from plowing, and found the water buckets empty, he pointed to the spring.

"Outside it was still fairly light. Pa figured we could get the water and be back before dark. But the spring was in a clump of pines, covered with honeysuckle. Needless to say, it was a scarey place after the sun went down.

"I could hear the pounding of my heart from running. It all but jumped from my chest when all of a sudden, right over my head, a hair-raising Mee . . ee . . oow filled the hollow. We dropped our buckets and ran, screaming like a couple of panthers. Naturally, time Pa got there with the gun, the cat was gone. But don't you ever believe that wildcat didn't weigh more than forty pounds. With that animal crouched over my head, I would have swore that it weighed a hundred, maybe more."

Spellbound, Bob and I sat, two towheaded kids with bare

feet dangling over the edge of the porch. When Uncle Ben went to the edge of the porch to get rid of some tobacco juice, we were afraid the conversation might turn to more timely things, such as when to plant beans and corn. But Father went inside to study his sermon, and when Uncle Ben cleared his voice, we knew he was wound up for another adventure.

"One of the most interesting varmints in these parts is the fox," he said. "No wonder folks calls him sly. For one thing, a fox isn't seen much in daytime. But the most unusual thing is the fact that he can charm a squirrel right out of a tree. I witnessed this once; otherwise, I wouldn't have believed it."

Pointing westward where a dark rim of mountains was outlined in the moonlight, he said, "I was hunting in that timber when I saw a young squirrel peering out of a hole in a red oak tree. Moving quietly, I set my sight on him, but just when I was ready to pull the trigger, a fox came slinking out of the undergrowth. He hadn't seen me, and I kept well out of sight. Next thing I knew, that fox fell on the ground and began to roll over and over. To my astonishment, the squirrel began to edge his way down the tree, teasing almost, dashing down, then up. Finally, unable to control himself, he let go of the tree and fell right into that fox's open mouth."

This story left Uncle Ben rather dry, and when he went to the kitchen for water, I heard Father ask whether he had finished breaking the corn land.

"That I did," he said. And to reassure Father of his farming methods, which were laced with superstition also, he said, "Did I show you the ribbon I won for the best corn in Newton county?"

"I believe so," Father said, knowing full well the old man had shown it a half dozen times.

"I won that ribbon the last year I farmed for myself," Uncle Ben said.

When he returned to his seat on the porch, he said, "You young'uns may not see the value in that old blue ribbon.

But knowing how to farm right has helped put two boys through college. That's a heap more education than I have ever had." Then smiling at some distant memory, he said, "There is quite a story behind the field of corn that won that ribbon. It is hard to tell how much corn I would have had if the groundhogs hadn't started eating at it. They didn't bother it until the moon started fillin'; then, man alive, I would find five or ten bushels of half-eaten roasting ears strung out along the rows.

"One night I took my shotgun, and I sat down to wait, determined to bag every varmint that showed its head. The moon climbed overhead, lighting up the field. Finally, I heard twigs breaking, so I raised my gun and set it dead on two yellow eyes I saw at the edge of the thicket. Just when I was ready to pull the trigger, I stopped, unable to believe my eyes. There stood a groundhog as yellow as Old Red's calf, and it was twice as big as most varmints of its kind. I tried to pull the trigger, but that animal walked past me, as courageous as you ever saw. Call it superstition or whatever you will. I didn't have the guts to kill him."

"Did you ever kill a snake?" Bob asked.

The old man chuckled. "Did I ever kill a snake, you ask. Son, I am going to tell you about the biggest snake I ever saw. It was right after me and Ollie married. Lawdy, when I think of how little me and that little woman started out with, it nearly scares me to death. Funny thing though, we were so in love, we thought we were rich. So, there we were, on a hillside farm, trying to make a living with one old mule. That rascal would jump a five-rail fence and be gone every morning of the world. Finally I got tired of chasing him, so I tied a log on his front leg and turned him into the barn lot for the night.

"Next morning when I went out to look for him, I saw marks that looked like the log being dragged down a sandy path. As it turned out, the mule was still in the lot. What I followed was a rattlesnake that was as big around as a fence post.

"I killed that snake, and for a long time Ollie was afraid to set foot outside the cabin door. She had heard that snakes usually travel in pairs, and she was afraid its mate might be under the house or thereabout.

"But as bad as a rattlesnake is, he is to be feared no more than the hoop. Mind you, I have never had any encounters with this snake. But I have heard it said that a hoop snake can plunge his tail into a tree, and the tree will be dead in fifteen minutes. Like I said though, I have had no dealings with a hoop, but I once had a run-in with a blue racer.

"I might not ought to tell you kids this, but I was playing hooky from school when it happened. I told sister Mary I had the stomachache, to go on without me; and I was eating my fill of wild grapes when I felt something cold and clammy wiggle across my foot. When I saw a blue racer on my bare foot, I just about jumped out of my overalls. I was so scared I paid no attention to where I was heading. Next thing I knew, it had chased me up to my yard gate. After that snake scare and a striping with Pa's razor strap, you can bet I never bypassed school anymore."

While Bob and I were digesting the snake story, a pack of hounds bayed past our place, hot on the heels of some animal. Suddenly there was a yelp, then silence, and the hills reeked with the pungent odor of skunk. Bob and I grabbed our noses, but Uncle Ben talked on. "For goodness sakes, don't ever let anyone tell you a skunk is harmless as long as you hold his tail down," he said. "I had heard that all of my life. One day on the way to Sunday school, me and some buddies found a baby civet cat in the middle of the road. He was a friendly little fellow, not afraid or anything, so we decided to catch him. We three boys hemmed him up, and I held his tail down. But that little rascal ruined my Sunday suit, and when we walked into that meetin' house, we broke up church."

After the skunk story, Uncle Ben fell silent, as though he had run down and was now content with his own thoughts. But one of our classmates had brought a turtle to school that day, and Bob was eager to tell Uncle Ben all about it. "We are studying turtles in science," Bob said.

"I could have told you all you needed to know," the old man interrupted. "There are seven kinds of meat in a turtle, and he is a mean animal. If he ever clamps down on a finger, he won't let go until it thunders."

Determined to get my two cents into the conversation, I said, "My teacher calls a turtle a reptile, not an animal."

"Pshaw," Uncle Ben said. Then pushing me out of the way so he might see the face of his watch in the moonlight, he said, "If you kids are planning to go to school tomorrow, you had better be off to bed." When we began to object, he said, "If you will remind me tomorrow night, I have a few more stories you might find interesting. Being city children, I guess these stories are right educational for you."

Later, when Mother had tucked Bob and me in our beds, she returned to the "front room" to sit with Father. Through the thin walls I heard her say, "Dennis, I wish you would have a talk with Ben. I realize he is old, he is a good worker, and I honestly feel sorry for him, knowing how he misses his wife. But I don't like the yarns he is feeding our children. Why, in time they won't know the truth when they hear it. I have spoken to him about it, but he doesn't seem to know what I am talking about."

In the stillness of the night, I heard the rustling of pine needles outside my window. Then Father spoke and I marveled that such a big man could always sound so gentle. He said, "Of course Ben doesn't know what you are talking about. The old man tells the truth as he has heard it. We can't change him, Amy. Besides, considering he is the only male member of my church and a member of our family, I would suggest you leave well enough alone."

Mother wasn't one to argue. "Maybe you are right," she said. "Come to think of it, I guess there are worse sins than stretching the truth, but I can't think of anything, unless it's chewing tobacco—and he does that, too."

When Father made no comment, she said, "You know I

am not one to question the will of God. But for the children's sake, I do wish we could have gone to the city, a small town, anywhere but here."

Curled in my warm, soft feather bed, I caught the disappointment in Mother's voice. From other evenings, I could see my parents, Mother with her sewing on one side of the oil lamp, Father with the Bible on the other side. He was as dark as she was blonde; she came just to his shoulder, and folks said they made a fine looking couple. I could imagine the disappointment in her blue eyes, and I felt guilty about loving the mountains so much. The way she kept saying "for the children's sake, I wish we hadn't come here" didn't seem right somehow because I knew that deep down she was more concerned for herself, and that is not to imply she was a selfish person. It was simply that nothing in Mother's background had prepared her for a backwoods ministry and having to get along with very little. The only child of a prominent surgeon, Mother had grown up in an elite, Fort Smith area. Her friends came from the country club set, and she and Father would never have met had not their parents been of the same faith.

Grandma and Grandpa Wilson lived on a peach farm north of Clarksville. The young folks met at a church camp and were married right after high school. Bob arrived a year later, and I came on the scene just before his second birthday.

When Father surrendered to the ministry, Mother did not feel the call. But she saw a change in her husband, and she feared God too much to object.

A Texas seminary was discussed, and Mother agreed to use half of the small legacy Aunt Pearl had left to Father. Bob and I, who were six and eight, listened to their moving plans, and we could hardly wait to get to the Lone Star State, certain the Texas city would still be a frontier town with cowboys and ten-gallon hats.

After what seemed like years of talk, Father quit his foreman job at a furniture factory. Then we children had our first train ride.

I remember being disappointed at the lack of cowboys and having to live in a small apartment; however, the rest of my memories of those four years are vague. Most of them have to do with the long, sleepy miles we traveled to some tiny village where Father would preach. Mother kept saying, "Sit up children. Just think, in a few more months Daddy will be called to a lovely church with a nice parsonage, probably in Fort Smith or Little Rock."

Father smiled as she talked, but he kept an open heart to God's leading. When we children asked where we would be living next, he would say, "I don't know yet where God wants us to serve. But I promise, wherever it is, it will be all right."

As it turned out, he wasn't given too much choice, and Father took that as a positive indication of God's guidance.

He graduated midterm in the early part of 1928. People were feeling the pinches of the coming depression, and preachers with good supporting churches weren't moving around much. We had stored our furniture at Grandpa Wilson's when we went to Texas, so we went back there. Father made application to two or three churches. When February came without word, he began to pace the floor. One day a childhood friend, Robert Revet, then pastor of a small church outside of Clarksville, spoke to Father about starting a new ministry in Newton county.

At that time Newton county was probably one of the country's remotest areas. There were no railroads in the county, and not one all-weather road. But having grown up in the Ozark foothills, Father had long been enamored with the mountain folk, and he was ready to accept the challenge of this new ministry.

When Dad broke the news to us right after supper, Grandma and Grandpa found an excuse to leave us alone. Bob and I jumped for joy, but Mother shook her head. "You have got to be kidding," she whispered. Dad's dark-lashed blue eyes had a determined gleam, and a look of terror spread across Mother's face. "There will be no close neighbors, no doctor if one of the children gets sick, a low-grade school; and whatever will we live on?"

Dad was pacing up and down the kitchen floor. He paused, and running a nervous hand through his dark hair, he said, "Robert's congregation has promised fifteen dollars a month."

"What on earth will you support on fifteen dollars?" Mother cried. "Certainly not a family of four."

Afraid that Mother would spoil our chance of living in the hill country, I listened from my chair at the end of the red-checked table. "Daddy will take care of us," I ventured.

No one seemed to hear; but when Father spoke, I was certain that my faith had not been misplaced. "Our own little congregation will be able to help some."

"What congregation?" Mother cried. "Where will we live in that God-forsaken country?"

Father's blue eyes begged for understanding. "I've got that all figured out. I will go on ahead of you and the children. I will hold a protracted meeting in the schoolhouse and make arrangements to use that building until we can build a church. Robert says there are a number of dedicated Christians who are praying for a church, so the organizing of a small group should be easy."

When Mother spoke, I could tell by the change in her tone that she was fighting to understand. "You know I am not one to go against the Lord's will, but you still haven't said where we will live."

"I was coming to that," he said. "I thought we could use the rest of Aunt Pearl's money to buy a small farm. With the right location, we could set a church building on a piece of the land. When we are ready to move on, we can sell the rest of the place. It's like money in the bank really. But you are right; the main reason I am suggesting the farm is because we can't live on Robert's offering. I will find someone to sharecrop; having someone to raise our food will help a good deal."

In the end, Mother agreed, but only because her religious

convictions would not allow her to refuse. In addition to her fears, Mother regretted her lack of college training, and she coveted Aunt Pearl's money for her children's education. But Father saw the money, like everything else he owned, as being sent from God. He was certain the Lord expected him to use it in the mountain work.

A few days later, he set out on one of Grandpa's horses. He held his revival meeting and organized a church with three women, three children, and Uncle Ben.

Father liked the old man from their first meeting. When Ben mentioned that he would like to sharecrop the following year, Father asked him to work for us. "Be glad to," the old man said, "and I know a good farm you can buy reasonable enough. German immigrants built the house forty years ago. They didn't go in for anything shoddy, so the house is a heap better than most you'll find. As I recollect, there are five large rooms, a stone cellar underneath, and it has a pump on the back porch. The land is good, too, with some creek bottom and plenty of upland pasture."

When Father looked the place over, he knew it was the best he would find, but twenty acres of meadowland sold him on the farm. Not knowing that Father planned someday to build a church on his land, the owner mentioned the meadowland cautiously. "There is a strip of meadowland, and though it is inconveniently located, it is included in the price. We bought it years after we homesteaded the rest of the place. Although it makes fine hay, it doesn't touch the rest of the property," Anna Gobel said.

As it turned out, the grassland lay in the valley between the store and the blacksmith shop. Father saw it as the future site of the Holly Oak Baptist Church.

When Father came for us and showed us the farm, Mother liked the place; and she fell in love with snowy-haired Anna. A frail looking little lady, with a crown of white braids, Anna insisted that we were to have dinner with her.

Later, around the table, she told how our farm came into being.

As a child, Anna had met her future husband on board ship as two German families made their way to the Pennsylvania coal mines. "A few years later, we heard of free land to be homesteaded in Arkansas," she said, "so both families came south.

"I was sixteen when Herman asked me to marry him. Of course, I had planned to marry him all along," she laughed, "for he was beautifully blonde and as straight as a pine." Her violet eyes took on a youthful sparkle as she recalled her wedding. "In preparation for the wedding, Herman homesteaded this land," she said. "He cleared the creek bottom and built a three-room house.

"During the next eight years I bore two boys and two girls. We had saved a little money, and the log cabin was getting crowded, so we decided to build this house. When the carpenters came to figure the cost, Herman surprised me by saying, 'I want a pump on the back porch. I am tired of my wife having to go so far to wash.' I had carried our wash to a spring a quarter of a mile away. So you can imagine I have loved that pump."

"I will think of you every time I use it," Mother said. Then Anna told how her love had not lived to enjoy his new home. A year later, he was driving a load of logs to town and his team of oxen became frightened. Leaving the trail, they plunged down a ravine.

Time had long since healed the pain of that separation, and Anna said, "All in all, I have been very happy here. I stayed on when the children established homes of their own. Until recently the land has given me a small income. But there isn't much money to be had these days. No one wants to rent, but there's always someone pestering me to run their cattle here for free."

As we talked around Anna's table, she suddenly paused. Turning her attention to Mother, she said, "Foolish old woman that I am, I have done all the talking. What about you, my dear? How do you think you will like living in my house?"

Without hesitation, Mother said, "Frankly, I don't care for the rutted trails and the unbridged creeks that lead to your door, because they make automobile travel impossible in winter through spring. But I like your house, and I have a feeling we will be very happy here."

So Father spent the last of his inheritance. The sale included two milk cows, two steers, a mule, a couple of sows, and some laying hens. And Anna gave Mother all of her fruit jars.

We moved about the middle of February, and a few days later Mother enrolled Bob and me in school. Though it was of no concern to my brother or me, I can see why Mother was worried. The two teachers had less than a high school education, and we would be walking a total of five miles daily over some of the roughest terrain Mother had ever seen.

Only shortly before we came had the traditional log school been abandoned for the tiny, two-room, frame building. But there was much to be said for this little school. Passing the old, gray building, we were reminded of an era forever gone, while the freshly painted, two-roomer suggested better things to come. When we met Miss Sally, the slender young woman who would be my teacher, she said, "The children won't have to go to the spring for water anymore. Last summer, some of the men dug a well on the grounds. Older boys will keep the water barrels filled. Every child must bring a drinking glass."

From the first day we loved that school, and whatever adjustments there were we easily made. But Mother was older, and the question of whether or not there would be any school troubled her. When the creeks were too full or the weather too blizzardly, we children simply could not go.

But for the most part, we were tucked into warm clothing, and we playfully marched down the mountainside, stopping now and then to crunch on an icicle that hung long and clear from the rocky bluffs. Other children joined us along the way. There wasn't a boot among us so our toes grew numb, and more than once Bob fell into the creek simply because he enjoyed falling in. There wasn't a one of us who could not cross a footlog as easily as a squirrel.

The school was nestled picturesquely in the valley. It had been built there for the hills' protection so the north wind would not whip the heat from the potbellied stoves kept red-hot by the wood supplied by our neighbors.

The "gym" was a great, open playground that extended into the woods. So long as we were present for classes, there were no boundaries. Knowing there were ravines and grapevine swings, Mother was troubled by the lack of boundaries. So we did not speak of our recesses too often.

Lunch in the form of fried egg or fried ham sandwiches came from a small lard pail. Not long after we came, one set of unfortunate children took up the wrong pail and actually brought a bucket of lard instead. While we were dividing up our sandwiches and fried pies so they could eat, one of the small boys delighted us by saying, "Sister, if us had some tatters, we could sop it."

As the preacher's children, Bob and I enjoyed a certain popularity. Our teachers and most of the children were pleased to have the school serve a twofold purpose with preaching services on Sunday. Ozark schools had long been diversified in their use and of vast importance in the community life. Through the week it served as a house of learning. On Sunday where there were no churches available, it stood ready to strengthen spiritual lives, and all year around the school was a community center where all sorts of activities took place. Voting was done there; it served as a theater when teachers decided to put on a play; and should a house burn, there were pie suppers or some other fund-raising event.

Though science and grammar had been added to the curriculum of the log school, we children were considered modern because we had art and music. But many of the old customs remained. Fridays were still given to spelling bees, ciphering matches, or literary programs.

"A literary" was a play with poems and readings, and each child was expected to take part. Usually these were presented on a Friday night. To receive our audience, ceiling lanterns were lighted, and the blackboard separating the "little room" from the "big room" was hooked up so that both rooms became an auditorium.

Entertainment of this sort brought people from miles around. During play practice on the chalk-scented stage, Miss Sally would sit below with the play in one hand and a lace handkerchief in the other. A victim of hay fever, she would dab lightly at her tilted nose. And speaking in a muffled sort of way, she would say, "Courtesy is one of the most important parts of delivery. So speak loudly and clearly." Most of the pupils loved Miss Sally. When her dreamy, brown eyes lit on us, we knocked ourselves out trying to please her. But even though she and all her pupils worked hard, Miss Sally just couldn't make an actor out of a potential plowboy. I recall many a bashful lad standing on one foot then the other, struggling with lines he had known as well as his own name only that afternoon. But his efforts were appreciated if the applause of our neighbors was any indication.

Though Sally Brock was a native of Holly Oak, the other teacher, Jane Cordell, man-sized redhead, came from Conway and boarded with the Corbatts. Miss Jane taught "the big room." Since some of the boys were in their late teens and had a reputation for having thrashed a teacher or two, Miss Jane carried a peeled oak stick.

School dismissed at 4 P.M. By the time we reached home, Father and Uncle Ben were doing the evening chores. Walking up the steep incline that led to our house, we would hear the sound of the ax. Old Shep, the dog we had inherited with Uncle Ben, was always waiting some distance from the house. At the sight of us coming around the bend, he would wag his tail and come bounding out to meet us.

In the late evening air the cowbell had a clear sound, and when I reached the back porch, old Pussy's fur felt good against my leg as she tried to beat me into the house.

On winter evenings we ate supper by lamplight. When

the dishes were put away, we did our homework at the kitchen table. The Gobels had built a great fireplace at one end of the room, and most cold evenings were spent in the kitchen.

When the fire burned low on the stone hearth, the lamp was blown out. We children climbed into our high straw mattress, topped off with a feather bed. One night in late February a snowstorm crept in, weighing down pine boughs and erasing all trails. When at the crack of dawn I heard the biting wind and saw the white outside, I lay back for a second nap. I knew there would be no school that day.

Spring came early that year. As we walked home along trails clean and pungent with pine, valley and hollow echoed with the voice of one plowman then another geeing and hawing their mules. The mating season added adventure to the long walks to and from school. We children paused to peek into a bluebird's nest, to count the furry balls in a rabbit's burrow, or to examine a tree for wild honey.

But for most adults, their leisure days were over. Uncle Ben had planted an early garden. One evening when we reached home, I heard him complaining because the day was Good Friday and the day beans should have been planted and could not be because our mule had died a few days before. Father had been visiting church prospects that afternoon, and he arrived about the same time as we kids. From the back steps I heard him say, "Your worries are over, Ben. I have been over to Mount Ridge, and the Lord has given a double blessing. I found a man that seemed really interested in the church, and he happened to have a horse I could get for Old Red's calf and that black steer."

I had been wanting a horse above all else, and I nearly tore the door down getting outside.

"What is he like?" I yelled.

"Just the prettiest thing you are likely to see," Dad grinned.

Always cautious, Uncle Ben asked the man's name. When Father told him that it was Donoldson, he said, "I know that feller, and I hate to sound gossipy, but that rascal would be interested in the devil if he could make a good horse trade."

I usually put a lot of stock in what Uncle Ben said, but Father's enthusiastic promise that I could ride the horse was such that I forgot the old man's warning, "That horse will probably be as mean as a wild-eyed steer."

The next day was Saturday. Since Bob and I considered daytime too short for sleeping, we were up before the first mockingbird announced dawn.

When the sun peeked into the cove where our farm lay, a truck lumbered up the bumpy road. When it stopped in front of the barn, Father said, "Come, I want all of you to see this velvet hunk of muscles."

He led the way to the barn. To be certain of a panoramic view, I climbed to the top of the rail fence, while Uncle Ben let down the end gate.

Father climbed the truck bed, untied the halter, and would have backed the horse down a loading chute. But the animal had other ideas. He reared up on his hind legs, pawed the air, then fell backwards out of the vehicle.

This got Father all unbalanced. He tumbled to the ground, and before he could pick himself up, the horse tore through the fence. His hind feet went into the air, and he didn't stop bucking until he reached the back side of the pasture.

I might have marked his shenanigans up to strange surroundings. But Uncle Ben noticed two things that marked him as a killer: The white of his eyes showed all around the iris, giving him a wild stare, and he had four white feet and a white nose. Shaking his head, the old man said,

"Four white feet and a white nose,
Might as well take off his hide
and feed him to the crows."

I doubted Father took much stock in such signs, but he sounded a bit uncertain when he spoke to the dried-up, sandy-looking driver. "Sir," he said, "I trust the horse has been broken the way you said he was, and I am expecting to meet you at church tomorrow morning."

"You can count on it, Preacher," Donoldson said. He barely touched Father's extended hand and then roared away in his truck.

The naming of the horse was left up to me, mainly because I wanted a horse far more than Bob did, or at least I had done more nagging. I admitted that I had thought of Dobbin the night before. But this horse with his energetic, brown body and prancing feet, added to the fact that he was supposed to be a killer, prompted the name Bullet.

When we settled the matter of the name, Father decided to work his horse. Ben had broken and harrowed some bean land before our mule died. With no difficulty Father caught Bullet and laid off a half dozen rows. Uncle Ben was working on a barn door. As I watched him tightening up a hinge, I noticed that he kept glancing nervously toward the field.

When Father came to the barn for some bean seed, I assumed the horse problem was as good as solved.

A few minutes later, Uncle Ben decided to move a bag of pig feed to the hog barn. I was chattering along at his side when all of a sudden we were startled half out of our wits by a thunderous sound and clanging metal. Looking toward the bean patch, I saw Bullet cutting a trail across the plowed ground while the planter disintegrated behind him.

Frozen to the spot, we waited for the fence to stop him, but it barely slowed him down. Dropping the feed bag, Uncle Ben dragged me behind an old wagon. The remains of the planter caught on the feed bag, and the ensuing cloud frightened Bullet all the more. Turning into an open gate, he bucked all the way across the pasture trying to get rid of the harness.

Luckily, Father was none the worse off. In spite of Ben's warning that the horse would kill someone, my father was undaunted. Dipping up a can of the hog feed, he went into the pasture and poured it into a trough. Since Bullet liked to eat as well as the next horse, catching him was never any problem. This time Father put him to a harrow, weighed down with a log. When he passed us, he said, "Don't worry. I am going to tire him out a bit before I put him to the plow. This will help him get used to the harness."

He opened the gate, and the harrow went creaking across the plowed ground. Bullet seemed as calm as the old gray mare. Around and around they went. Then we followed Father and Bullet to the field. Just when Uncle Ben seemed to be breathing easier, a rabbit jumped from a hole, brushing Bullet's legs as he went. The horse's nostrils quivered, and in a flash he was off again. The harrow and the log parted company, and a second later Bullet disappeared behind the barn.

That Father had run out of patience was apparent by the set of his mouth. "I'll kill that horse," he said, walking determinedly toward the barn.

I repeated the threat as the old man and I followed somewhat behind. Uncle Ben chuckled. "Now that is the least of my worries," he said. "You know the preacher wouldn't kill a flea; he wouldn't kill—a—flea," he whispered. But there, stretched out on the ground, was Father's velvet hunk of muscles, and Bullet's eyes were rolled back in his head as though he were dead.

For once Ben was speechless, and my voice was full of emotion. "I never dreamed you would really kill him!" I cried. Truly angry with my father for the first time, I turned accusing eyes on him. I said, "A preacher is not supposed to kill things."

Uncle Ben cleared his throat. "I know he was an ornery cuss," he began, "but killing a horse is bad luck. I would rather you hadn't done it."

Father surveyed our concerned faces with puzzled eyes. "I believe you two have gone as loco as this fool horse," he said. Then stooping, he cut the plow lines from around Bullet's neck and legs. Bullet's eyes rolled back into position, he gave a heave, and Uncle Ben and I saw what had happened. The tangled leather had thrown him, and in floundering about, he had nearly choked himself to death.

Getting his wind, Bullet staggered to his feet, shook his head, then wobbled off across the pasture.

By now, the day was too far spent to repair the damage. Dad decided to go to the store for more bean seed, and "just to get away from it all." "Don't expect me back before sundown," he told Mother, explaining that he would stop by the school on the way home and get the building ready for Sunday school and church.

Still perplexed, Father set off on his own two feet. When he returned at suppertime, he was riding horseback double with a man we had never seen before. In the kitchen, he introduced the sun-bronzed stranger. "This is Fred Granger," he said. "Fred is passing through these parts, and he needs a place to spend the night."

Taking strangers in was common practice in isolated Ozark country. Mother knew this, and without one question as to who the man might be, she added another plate to the already set table.

Like children everywhere, Bob and I loved company that had something interesting to say; Fred was a hero right out of the old West.

After supper we gathered around the lean, quick-smiling man, hoping for a story. He said, "I left home at sixteen. Now after twenty-six years, I am going back to Madison County to visit my aging mother."

Then he held us spellbound with stories of an illness in his youth that had forced him to live among the Comanches in Indian Territory, of punching cattle in Texas, and of bronc busting in Kansas. These stories led to our own recent adventure with Bullet, and I could see that Fred was more than interested.

Fred vowed that he had not met the horse he could not tame. Before the evening was over, he and Father had made a bargain. Should he break Bullet for riding, then the horse would be his for his older, more gentle Bell. Fred was so enthused with the idea that Father decided to use it as a means to get his new friend to attend church. He said, "You realize, of course, that I can't have you taming a horse on Easter Sunday. Looks like you will have to stay over until Monday and attend services with us tomorrow."

Always agreeable, Fred laughed his big, hearty laugh. "Looks like you have trapped me, Preacher," he said. Then his blue eyes were thoughtful as he looked back across the years. "I guess a little religion won't do me any harm. I haven't been inside a church since I left my mother's house—though she has written me regularly about it," he said.

So he went to church with us. After Sunday school his big, bass voice sang the hymns with gusto, and when Father preached of the cross and the love that nailed Jesus there, Fred's eyes never once strayed from the preacher's face. When the invitation was given, Father saw our new friend come down the aisle to accept Christ as Savior. With tears in his eyes, he said, "I want to be right with God when I meet my mother. She hasn't got many years left, and she has prayed for me for so long."

Next morning when the new Fred Granger threw his saddle across Bullet's quivering back, I knew the horse had met his match. The weekend visit was extended through Wednesday night prayer meeting. During this time Fred helped with the planting, and I witnessed some of the wildest riding I had ever seen. When Fred won, he rode away, leaving a lasting friendship and enough stories to quicken our hearts until some other living excitement came our way.

2.
Learning
Mountain
Ways

With Uncle Ben being the only male member of Holly Oak Baptist, Father had two passions: Number one was that of winning some menfolk, and number two was seeing a building stand on the land he had dedicated to that purpose.

 Since our farm was in an isolated area, over two miles from the main flow of the community, Father felt that the Lord had been leading when the Gobel's purchased the distant land years before. With conviction he said, "The Lord knew I would be coming later and would build a church on that property."

 Uncle Ben agreed that it was an ideal spot, laying the way it was between the blacksmith shop and the school. The combination grocery store and post office was just beyond that.

 As Father had hoped, our land had some good timber on it that could be made into lumber. "The only thing lacking is a group of interested men," he said. "If I could just figure out some way to get them inside the church house, then some might be converted," he would say. Several of the men would drive their families to church and then sit outside visiting under a shade tree while Father preached his heart out. Part of their reluctance to come inside came from the fact that many of the mountain men saw religion as something for women and children, but mainly, Father had not yet proven himself as worthy of their company. Though he had been raised on a farm not more than thirty miles away, Father's educated ways marked him as an outsider. Due to their love for a story in which someone made a fool of himself, rumors had it that Father had paid too much for his farm, and the fact that he had traded two yearlings for a wild horse completed the picture.

One day when Father entered the store, he heard someone say, "The reverend is like a lot of them city fellers. He came here with money. But the day he leaves, he'll be lucky to have a shirt on his back."

"I know what you mean," another said. "In a way I feel sorry for the likes of him. Them ornery land sharks advertises old pore land at an ungodly price. Along comes some ignorant cuss with money to burn, and he swallows the bait, hook, line, and sinker."

"They are to be pitied alright," another said, and the silence that fell on the crowd when Father was discovered was more painful than the gossip.

Father was a man who made friends easily, and the idea that he had been rejected on such flimsy grounds weighed heavily on his shoulders.

But Mother wasn't worried about the men. Though she had not wanted to come to the mountains, once she was settled there, she accepted her responsibility as Father's helpmate, and it was the women and children she hoped to do something about. Seeing their physical lot as nearly helpless, she felt they needed the church to motivate them toward better things. Except for Miss Sally and the other teacher, Mother knew of no one who had gone to high school, and few had completed eighth grade. Troubled by the lack of education in the community, Mother asked Sally why more children weren't finishing grade school. "There are several reasons," Sally said. "First of all, they are needed in the fields. Second, they haven't the money for books. Third, they get behind so that a sixteen-year-old may still be in sixth or seventh grade. Most of the girls are married by that age."

Mother had noticed that many of the women were weather-beaten and old looking, though barely out of their twenties. "I feel so sorry for them," she told Father. "They work in the fields until they feel the first pangs of labor. Then without the aid of a doctor they bear the child, a child whose dreams will never get over the tops of these mountains."

Accepting these women and children as her responsibility, Mother learned to milk, and we traded a calf for an aged horse so Father could operate a Sunday school wagon. Though Uncle Ben had farmed all of his life, he had never learned to milk. Mother rose early each Sunday, cooked a hearty breakfast for her family, and then did the milking while Uncle Ben fed the pigs and the chickens. Bob and I were making beds and doing dishes while off in the hills and hollows Father was rounding up women and children who had no transportation to church.

Later, when the bell summoned us to our Bible classes, Mother ushered the little ones into a cloak room. The children sat circled around her, and she taught them stories from the Bible, showing how much they ought to love God because he loved them. To prove God's love on levels they would understand, she used the streams, the hills, and the graceful pines as illustrations.

One day she said, "God has been especially good to you children, for nowhere else in all the world is one likely to find a prettier place in springtime than right here in the hills."

Mother held most of the young faces in rapt attention, but one lad sat sullen and angry because his mother had made him leave the men under the shade tree and come inside. Mother had pretended not to notice his anger. Now he drawled, "What's so purtty about this old place?"

32

Undaunted, Mother said, "That is a good question, Elbert. We will have to go to the window to answer it."

Reluctantly, the boy dragged himself to the window, and the rest of the children gathered eagerly about. Giving Elbert her full attention, Mother said, "Remember how March roared in like a windy old lion, tossing uncertain clouds above the leafless trees?"

"I remember," he said. "I wuz hopin' it would snow, but it rained instead." Interested in spite of himself, Elbert pushed a brown mane out of his eyes for a clearer picture of the world about him.

"You are right," Mother said. "It rained and it rained during the month of March. Now April is here, and the mountains are clothed in springtime green. On the way to Sunday school, I saw a swift, little creek all blue or green. Who knows what color water is when it is rushing over smooth, brown stones?"

A quietness had settled over the group as each child considered the outside world. Then one of the men gave a "hee haw" that echoed across the hollow, and Elbert's lip drooped again. "I know what color that old creek is," he said. "It's clur; that's what color it is—any simpleton knows that."

Choosing to ignore his remark, Mother turned the subject to other nature objects. "How many of you like to pick wild flowers?" she asked.

Several hands shot up. Mother said, "This is the month for it. The meadows are full of candy-striped Johnny-jump-ups, and shy little violets have pushed back their leafy covers to nod happily in the sun."

Turning to the boys, she said, "Listen, hear the frogs croaking their throaty songs? Only yesterday, I saw a multi-colored rainbow making a halo over Woods Mountain. Did any of you children see it?"

Mother felt a tug at her skirt, and a small boy said, "I didn't see the rainbow. But I saw a honeybee, and I followed him to his tree. There is honey in a big hollow oak, and my pa is going to cut it."

"Wonderful," Mother said. "That means the warm sun has awakened all the bees. At first they stretched their wintery legs to see if they were working properly. Then they tried out their wings, making a buzzing, fanning sound. 'It is time to work,' something said to the bee. He arched into the air, and away he went because God planned it that way."

Mother tried to put color and appreciation into her Bible teaching, and the little children loved her for it. But a group of mothers cornered her one Sunday. Nina Cocks, a red-faced, sun-bleached blond, said in behalf of the group, "Miz Wilson, we would rather you stuck strictly to plain Bible teaching. We don't go in for this tomfoolery about frogs croaking and violets kicking back their 'kivers.' "

Mother was stunned and hurt, almost to tears. But she was determined to teach her class the way she thought small children should be taught. In her sweetest voice, she said, "I appreciate what you have told me. It shows that you are interested in your child's spiritual training—a lot of parents couldn't care less." She explained the child's short attention span and then went on to say, "The Bible story takes about thirty minutes. I teach it carefully, never adding or subtracting. Then we turn to nature objects that will apply to the child's everyday living. I think you will probably agree that Jesus made use of this kind of teaching when he gave us the parables."

Two women stood behind Mother. Nettie Corbatt, wife of the man who ran the neighborhood store, and Miss Sally, my schoolteacher. Since these women carried a great deal of influence, Mother relied on them when she needed help in other areas. She had learned she was dealing with a proud people, and while their clothes and way of speaking were backwoodsy to her, Mother's lack of practical knowledge seemed downright ignorant to them. She had to admit she knew nothing about making soap, lard, sausage, hominy, molasses, or how to set a hen. These were essential chores in Ozark country, and no woman would knowingly admit complete ignorance in these areas. Knowing this, Mother tried to hide her lack of practical knowledge, but it had ways of slipping out.

One Sunday, the women paused on the school steps to discuss baby chicks. Nina Cocks said, "I think I will kill a fryer when I get home. They are a little small for frying, but the pork is all gone and we are getting meat hungry."

"I know what you mean," Nettie Corbatt said. "But my biddies are away too small. Why, the roosters aren't any larger than a good-sized quail."

"You are still ahead of me," Mother said. "I set two hens. One started out with ten eggs, the other with eight. I waited until the incubating period was up, and then I looked underneath the pecking old sisters. So help me, there was a dozen or more eggs under each hen. Some of the eggs were broken, all were dirty, and none had hatched. Do you suppose the setting hens went right on laying?"

A snicker rippled among the women, and even Sally, Mother's best friend, stared for a second, unable to believe that anyone could be so dumb. Then she said, "My dear, there are certain things one should do before one sets a hen. First, you mark the eggs, then you will know whether or not fresh eggs are being laid in the nest. It is not unusual for a laying hen to crowd off a hen that is setting. So watch the eggs, all fifteen of them, for that is the usual number one puts under a hen."

While Mother was waiting for her face to cool, Nina Cocks said, "If you are planning to raise a batch of chickens this year, you had better hurry. April is almost gone, and May chickens are no good."

"Why not?" Mother asked. Then she wished she had kept quiet, for Nina was shaking her head as though the preacher's wife was hopeless. "It is just one of those things, like knowing geese should lay their first eggs before March 17 or they are bound to have a bad year," explained Nina. "Oh, that reminds me," she continued, "I hear you are short of stock feed, so I put two bushels of corn in your wagon."

I overheard the conversation, and on the way to the wagon

I tried to visualize a goose having a bad year. But for the life of me I couldn't imagine what might happen. I was glad when Mother spoke to Uncle Ben about it. We were riding home in the wagon with Mother, Father, and Uncle Ben—all of them in the spring seat. Bob and I were sitting on a quilt in the back. Uncle Ben, dressed in striped overalls, snapped the lines, urging the horses forward. Then he spoke, "It's just an old saying," he said. "Can't say that there is any truth in it either. But there is one well-known sign concerning geese that I do believe. It goes like this:

More downy the feathers from geese or ducks,
If in the new moon they are carefully plucked."

"I will remember that," Mother said. Then she told the men about her blunder with the setting hen. "Never, have I felt so dumb," she said. "No wonder these people think I am a citified dunce."

Uncle Ben chuckled, and Father put his arm around her. "Don't let it throw you," he said. "If it's any comfort to you, I sometimes feel the same way, and I was raised on a farm. For instance, an old farmer set me back on my heels just the other day. Trying to make conversation when I stopped by an oat patch where the man was working, I said, 'I read an interesting thing about oats the other day. The writer claimed that an acre of grain can lift six and a half tons of water a day.'

"The farmer pushed back his straw hat, and his leathery face wrinkled in an amused grin. Finally he said, 'You can tell that feller there ain't that much water in this dad-burned field.' Before I could comment, he said, 'I'll tell you something else that writer ain't likely to know. A person had better plant his oats in the light of the moon, or he won't raise enough to feed a coon.' "

Uncle Ben agreed with the farmer, and since Mother and Father saw themselves at a disadvantage when they tried to witness to the people, they failed to see any humor in the saying. But Bob and I thought it was hilarious. We fell over on the quilt, and we rolled and chanted, "Better plant your oats in the light of the moon, or you won't raise enough to feed a coon."

When Father grew weary of our loud nonsense, he waved Uncle Ben's horse whip in our direction. This sobered us somewhat, but we sniggered until we reached home.

Though Mother lacked practical knowledge for mountain living, she was a good organizer, and this won a great deal of respect from the women. First, she organized the women's missionary union. Most of the people were unbelievably poor. Since there would be no offerings for foreign missions, Mother decided to focus their attention on community needs. Falling crop prices, frost, and drouth left the people with little money.

One Sunday, Mother invited Sally to have dinner with us, and they spent the afternoon discussing project possibilities. Sally mentioned quilt making since most of the women were real artists in this area. "But materials are hard to come by," she said.

This comment started the wheels turning in Mother's head. She remembered Father's foreman days at the furniture factory and the barrels of upholstery scraps they had given to anyone for the asking. "Of course, we will make quilts," Mother said. "The women will do wonderful things with those pieces of brocades, velvets, and mohair. The quilt tops will be so heavy that we won't need cotton for padding."

"What pieces?" Sally wanted to know, for Mother in her excitement had forgotten to explain. When Mother explained her idea, Sally was delighted with it, and so was Father.

That night Mother addressed two letters to Fort Smith. One went to the furniture factory, asking for the scraps, with the promise that she would pay the postage. The other letter went to her mother, asking Grandma Tate to speak to her missionary group about sending thread and lining materials as a part of their own mission program.

In less time than Mother had anticipated, Grandma's letter came saying a box was on its way. A few days later a notice came from the plant superintendent indicating that two barrels of scraps were on their way.

Allowing time for arrival of the materials, Mother announced a quilting to be held at our house.

Four days before the gathering, the box and the barrels arrived, and Uncle Ben went for them in the wagon.

When he came back from the post office, Father helped carry the things into the living room, and we gathered about, feeling like children around a Christmas tree.

When Grandma's church box was opened, a clean starchy smell met our nostrils. There was layer after layer of soft cotton flannels (some florals), boxes of bright colored yarns for tacking comforters, and some soft, white materials that Mother said could be made into underwear.

Father had great respect for Mother's parents. Although he had never accepted personal help from them, he was delighted with the church gift. But more than anything, he was pleased with the way Mother was taking hold. Teasing her, he said, "Now I know why I brought you along on this venture. I dare say those boxes of scraps will win more souls than a year's preaching."

Mother was kneeling beside the box, and her blue eyes sparkled with a child's excitement. Always careful to put him out front, she reached for his hand. Kissing it, she said, "You will plant, I will do my best to water, and one day God will give the increase."

We were still digging around in the gifts when Uncle Ben came in from the barn where he had been taking the team from the wagon. Reaching into his pocket, he handed Father a letter. "I was about to forget this," he said.

Father went to his high-back rocker and tore off the end of the envelope. When he read the letter, he was glad it had come with the boxes, for the excitement would ease the burden of its message. When he spoke, Father's voice was husky with disappointment. "This letter concerns all of us, so I guess we had all better hear it," he said. Then he began to read.

Dear Brother Wilson:

Due to a church split, a new pastor, and general hard times among our members, it is my sad duty to inform you that no more checks will be coming from this church. I would recommend that you get in touch with the home mission board. They may be able to help you.

For a stunned moment Father and Mother stared at each other. They had been on the field less than three months, and already their support was gone. They both knew it was a moment for decision making. For though fifteen dollars was a small amount, it had kept staples in the pantry. "What will we do?" Bob asked.

Sensing the fear in the child's voice, our parents rose to the occasion. "Do?" Mother laughed. "We will work harder, raise our own food, and we will build a church."

These were the words Father needed to hear. "We won't starve," he assured us. To prove the point, he counted our blessings. "We have plenty of butter, milk, and eggs; and the garden is coming in."

As though we needed more assurance, Mother said, "We can use Nina's offering for bread."

Puzzled, Father said, "What offering?"

"The two bushels of corn Nina Cocks contributed. I guess I forgot to tell you," Mother said.

"But that was for the horses," Bob said, still uncertain.

"Horses, horses," Mother grew silly for our benefit. "Horses can eat grass. Your daddy is taking that corn to the mill."

Uncle Ben had been sitting quietly through all of our planning. When he found the right moment for some words of his own, he said, "I have a few dollars, and you should know what is mine is yours."

By this time, Uncle Ben was an accepted part of the family, even by Mother. But my parents had no intentions of taking the old man's savings.

"I appreciate that, but I need your help more than I need

your money," Father said. "I want you to teach these kids how to work." Then focusing his attention on us, he said, "So far, Ben has done most of the farm work. With a little money coming in, I figured we could get along by raising a few potatoes, some garden stuff, and some grain for the stock. But we are going to have to branch out, and Uncle Ben is too old to do all the hoeing and the picking. We will all have to work, especially since I am thinking of planting cotton in part of the creek bottom."

"I will work real hard," I promised, feeling even more a part of my family because now I was partly responsible for its welfare.

"So will I," Bob said, and the matter was settled.

On quilting day I helped Mother with her part of the potluck dinner, and I then went to the porch swing to watch the road. School was out now, and I was hoping some of the children would come also. Except for Sunday afternoon when I had a guest or went to some child's house, I had to be content with my brother's company. Mountain children worked beside their parents, and since we were learning to do the same, this made a day of play seem extra special.

As I had hoped, Nettie Corbatt brought Sybil, a slender girl with brown, almond-shaped eyes and two Indian-black braids. Sybil was about my own age, and I loved her for three reasons: She was beautiful; she was a lot of fun; and perhaps more important, her father owned the grocery store. This made her very popular, and I considered her friendship an honor almost beyond me.

Nina Cocks brought Phil and Bill, twin boys, Bob's age.

When the women went inside, I called Bob from the field where he was helping Father plant watermelons. Delighted at the sight of his friends, my brother said, "You guys want to play hide-and-seek, or would you rather look for crawfish in the creek?"

The twins began to roll up their overalls. "We don't want to play with no girls, that is for shore," one of them said. Taking his words as a personal insult, Sybil and I ignored them from the porch swing. But the truth was, I was very fond of Phil and Bill, and I had been hoping to play hide-and-seek.

When they closed the pasture gate behind them, I suggested a game of jacks, but Sybil's eyes were on the road, and she did not hear me. I started to repeat myself, but she said, "See that woman and that baby Miss Sally is bringing with her?"

I looked, then nodded without special interest. The women are going to make a quilt for her and some baby clothes, too," my friend said.

"Why are they making things for her?" I asked, still more interested in a game of jacks.

"Cuz they are real hard up," Sybil said. "Mama says they are living in that old shack near Dar's Mill. I didn't think anyone could live in that place," she went on, "but they moved in last week."

I was still more interested in play than charity, but Sybil's next words aroused my curiosity. "Would you believe she is only sixteen and that she has been married for two years?"

Sally and the new woman were coming through the yard gate, so Sybil dropped her voice to a whisper. "Her man's been out of work ever since the river got out of its banks down in Cardins Bottom. Mama said the woman's milk dried up, and when the baby wouldn't eat beans and such, the little thing nearly starved to death. Look when she goes by. That baby is the most pitiful sight you will ever see."

Mother had seen them coming. When she came to the door to greet Sally, the school teacher said, "This is Millie Lee, a newcomer to our community."

The young woman fingered the one button on her dingy blouse, trying to conceal an unsightly undergarment and a lily-fair bosom.

From the swing, I observed the stranger with compassionate eyes. She looked more like fifty than sixteen. She was so gaunt there seemed to be nothing between her bones and her sun-baked freckles. As Sybil had warned, the baby was enough to break a person's heart. She was a listless skeleton, and only her creamy-blonde hair showed any normal growth. When she saw us children in the swing, her toothless mouth puckered in a smile. Though she was nearly two, her boney legs would not hold her up, and she whined her misery all the time.

Inside, Millie was introduced to six other women, and then Sally drew Mother back to the porch. "I want to explain Millie's being here," she said. "They are living in that old sawmill shack. Her man's going to log up there. In the way of furniture, they have a stove and a homemade table. They have no bedding to speak of, no decent clothing, and no food until he gets paid."

Mother was thoughtful. "We will have to do something," she said. "I have milk and butter to spare, and I suppose I could give a few eggs even though I usually trade them for sugar and such. Yes, I'll give what I can. One of the children can carry milk and butter to them every other day."

"We will speak to the other women about contributing," Sally said.

"Yes," Mother hurried on, "we will have to make a couple of quilts for that poor soul, and some things for the baby."

The two women went back inside. Mother opened up her sewing machine, and over the whirl of it, Sybil and I could hear the women talk as they worked. "My mother would die at the thought of a machine-made quilt top," Nettie said.

"I know what you mean," Nina said. "But, of course, this is an emergency, and it would be foolish not to use the faster method."

After a while Sybil suggested that we join the boys at the creek whether they wanted us there or not. We kicked off our shoes so we would be all set for wading and hurried across the pasture.

As we feared, the boys still weren't eager for our company, and we had barely come into sight when Phil said, "If you don't want to get stung, you had better go back to the house."

"Stung by what?" I asked, determined to hold my ground.

"By yaller jackets," he said. "Look over your head. We are going to knock down that big nest."

Sybil and I looked up. Right over our heads was a swarming, cone-shaped mass. But we weren't easily frightened. "You'll get stung if we do," I said.

Bill joined his brother in the war against us. "We will not. We know a secret chant that hypnotizes yaller jackets."

"Yeah, we know a secret code," Bob said, feeling important because he knew something I didn't.

"We aren't leaving here until you tell us the secret code," Sybil said. Then she picked up a rock, aimed it between the twins, and it landed with a splash.

"You wet my overalls," Bill yelled. "Now get stung and see if I care." He grabbed up a stone and hurled it into the tree. Sybil and I ran, but the boys screamed:

"Jasper, whisper, jacket,
You can no more sting me
Than the devil can count sixpence."

To their sorrow, they later discovered they had knocked down a hornets' nest, and in that case they should have chanted:

"Hornet, hornet, don't sting me,
Sting that man behind that tree."

Leaving the boys with swollen faces, Sybil and I made our way back to the porch where we enjoyed a safer, though less exciting, hour in the swing.

When we tired of dragging our feet back and forth across the floor boards, we went inside to see how the quilting was coming along. We found one heavy top all ready for tacking. Mother had suspended a pair of quilting frames from a bedroom ceiling. The lining was stretched, the top was laid in place, and four women were threading darning needles with strands of heavy yarn.

After potluck, the first quilt was taken from the frames, and Mother hemmed it on the sewing machine. When it was finished, she placed it in Millie's arms. Tears welled up in the girl's eyes. "Thank you," she whispered to all the women around the room. "This means more to me than just getting a cover," she said. "You see, I ain't ever had showin' on how to make quilts and such. My maw died when I was six. Pa and my older brother took care of me to the best of their knowledge. But they kept me in the field most of the time. So I ain't ever had woman training to speak of."

Silence fell over the talking women. Choking back a tear, Sally finally said, "Then it's our pastor's wife you really should thank. For the idea began with her."

Before Mother could speak, the girl laid the quilt beside her fretting child and ran across the room to hug the preacher's wife. "Lord bless you," she said. "You have showed me that Pa's been all wrong about church folk. I used to want to go to protracted meetings, and he would always say, 'I don't see why. They ain't nothing but a bunch of hypocrites down there. I grant you, if they saw the likes of us stretched out dead, they wouldn't stop to bury us.' You have showed me that ain't true. You can count on me and the baby being in church next Sunday. But I can't say about my man. He has got a lot of Pa's notions."

Millie Lee was converted a few Sundays later, but her long-haired, ill-dressed husband would have nothing to do with the church.

From the day of the quilting bee, Mother was in. This gave her confidence and kept her mind alert for new ideas that might prove helpful to those in dire need.

The lack of books which kept many of the children from attending school bothered her. When a third barrel of scraps arrived, she approached the women with the idea of making a half dozen fancy tops to sell to Grandma Tate's club friends. "If this goes over, it would help buy school books," she said.

The women approved the idea, and when Grandma received her sample with bright-colored brier-stitching around each piece, she wrote back requesting a dozen.

The women worked long hours over those quilt tops, happy in the knowledge that when school started in the fall, there would be books for everyone.

The quilting project was so successful that Mother organized a handcraft club where ideas could be exchanged. Finally, with Grandma Tate's help, monthly speakers were brought in to present information on food preservation, basket making, cooking, and sewing. This program was not unlike the Home Demonstration clubs that soon followed. Women came from miles around to attend these Thursday potluck meetings, and a goodly number returned on Sunday, bringing their children to Sunday school.

3.
Gaining
the
Men's
Confidence

While Mother was working her way into the hearts of the womenfolk, Father was far from idle. The men took to him much more slowly, but he was learning through trial and error. After a few trips to the mill or the store, he discovered that Ozark men with their ability to find an amusing side to every story were excellent storytellers.

Since Father's parents had come from the Tennessee hills and his own youth had been spent in the Ozark foothills, Father knew some "tall tales" of his own. In this area he could compete with the best of the old-timers. Realizing this, he was determined to talk his way into their hearts.

One spring morning he pushed back his breakfast plate and announced that he was taking some of our donated corn to the mill. Father knew I had a nickel that was burning a hole in the sugar bowl. When I asked if I might go with him, he agreed.

In a world sparkling with dew diamonds, Father balanced a bag of corn across old Bell's rear. Then we climbed into the saddle. Horseback riding always seemed the greatest fun to me until I got into the saddle, and then I was always fearful. I clung to Dad's waist, and we wound our way down the mountainside.

Here and there the call of a bobwhite echoed across the ridge, and the flash of multicolored wings was seen as red-bird and meadowlark darted upward. Wildrose and honeysuckle sweetened the air, and the horse's hoofs clopped against the rocks. At last the sound of rushing water reached our ears, and the mill loomed ahead.

While Father was tying Bell to the hitching post, I shopped in a matchbox store all covered with tobacco signs. Lean, hooked-nose Ed Corbatt was putting away merchandise when I entered. All of the nail kegs circling the potbellied stove were empty, for the men had deserted them for the cooler bench built around the mill oak.

I paused before the stained candy case and, after some deliberation, decided on two bubble gums and three suckers. The smell of apples, piled high on a basket, made my mouth water. But they were out of the question, so I took my small, brown bag across the way where Father was setting his grain in line with several other bags.

Content with my purchases, I found a spot of moss in the oak shade. As I dropped to it, I heard Father say, "Hi Jack. How is your sick cow?"

Jack Kline, a Civil War veteran, was resting his whiskery chin on the curved handle of a homemade walking stick. "She is alright now. 'Tweren't nothing but lost cud," he said. "I give her a dishrag right after you called, Preacher. She was up and about next day."

"That's more than I can say for Paul Holmes' cow," another old-timer cut in. From where I sat, I studied the black, half-laced shoes of this aged man, and my nose caught the sweet smell of his chewing tobacco.

Fletcher Kindrick said, "Preacher, you may not know Paul. He is the feller that came here right after he finished agriculture school."

Father shook his head. "Don't believe we have met."

"Well," Fletcher continued. "Paul is like a lot of them city fellers. He is well posted on some things, but when it comes to doctorin' cattle, he is up the creek without a paddle.

"Last week I was squirrel huntin', and I came across one of his prize jerseys. When I saw she had lost her cud, I mosied on up to Paul's house, and I told him the cow needed a dishrag. He thanked me, but said he didn't believe in such remedies."

Laughter rippled out of Jack, and the snowy-haired Fletcher continued, "He said he was calling a veterinarian. Now I knew he needed a vet like a hog needs a sidesaddle, but what could I do?

"I mosied on home, and about sundown I saw a model-T go by. I knew it was Paul's cow doctor. It was mizzling rain. I had no business going out, but I wanted to hear what that feller would say.

"When I got there, the vet was looking down Cherry's throat. 'She is bloated,' he said, like he was telling me something I didn't already know.

" 'What do you think the trouble is?' Paul asked.

"The vet was all decked out in a ten-gallon hat and high heeled boots. You could tell he was a skinner. He said, 'Not too much wrong. The cow has lost her cud.' "

Pausing for a triumphant laugh, Fletcher said, "I gave a hoot that just about plagued Paul to death. But as crazy as I figured that scamp of a doctor to be, I never expected the remedy he prescribed."

"What in tarnation did he give her?" Jack asked.

"You won't believe it," Fletcher said, shaking so hard he had difficulty repeating the veterinarian's words. "He said— he said—'This cow needs a frog.' "

"A frog?" Jack hooted.

" 'A frog,' that scamp said. 'This cow needs a frog.' Then he opened a bait bucket and let a bullfrog hop down Cherry's throat. For a minute, I thought shore as shootin' she would choke to death. But the surprise of it all was that the frog brought the critter to her feet, and next day she was grazing with the rest of the herd. But the ribbing I gave old Paul makes it unlikely he will recommend the treatment to anyone else."

Father joined the laughter, but he could imagine the exaggerated stories that followed his adventure with old Bullet. Always on the lookout for a church prospect, he made a mental note to visit Paul Holmes. Meanwhile, he was determined to impress the motley two with a story of his own.

Shifting his long frame to a sidewise position so he could see both men, Father said, "Speaking of Paul Holmes reminds me of an old boy named Paul Brinks. My dad sawed logs with him some years ago. Paul was only seventeen, but he was as stout as a mule. One day Paul got the hiccoughs while they were working, and they got so bad he could hardly pull the saw. According to Papa, he tried sips of water, holding his breath, and running around in circles. Nothing helped."

As Father talked, Fletcher's whiskered mouth was spread in a grin, and he nodded his head knowingly. "Your pappy should have tried making him mad," he said.

"Hold your horses. I am coming to that," Father said. "When they had tried everything else, Papa remembered that anger was supposed to cure hiccoughs. So he made up a tale he figured would get old Paul's goat. " 'Paul,' he said, 'Hoot Vinson is out to get you. He claims you stole that coon dog he ordered from Tennessee.'

"You could have cooked an egg on the boy's face. He stopped hiccoughing, and Papa started to tell him it was all a makeup. But Paul stopped him cold. 'I wonder how Hoot found out,' he said. 'Truth is, I just borrowed the dog, didn't really steal him a-tall. Guess though, I had better be taking the critter home. If Pa finds out, he will whale the daylights out of me.' "

This was the sort of story Jack and old Fletcher enjoyed most. For the first time since his coming to the mountains, Father enjoyed a moment of social glory. Fletcher laughed so hard the tobacco juice ran down his dingy beard, and

51

Jack would have toppled off the bench if Father had not caught him. "That's a goodun, Reverend," he said. "Reminds me of Preacher and his dog story."

"That's one I ain't been educated to," Fletcher said. "But if it has anything to do with Preacher, it's bound to be a goodun."

Father could see Jack was eager to get on with the story, but Fletcher felt the story would be more effective if Father knew something about the man.

"Preacher is part evangelist, part farmer, but mostly hunter, which is fortunate, considering his hillside land is as pore as a rail. He has a pack of hounds and eight kids at last count. But Preacher is a Baptist, and I 'spect you ought to call on him Reverend."

Father was delighted that the old man had brought up church. While he was jotting down directions, Jack went on with his story.

"One night Preacher and a couple of his boys hunted until midnight. When the dogs didn't tree anything, they gave up and went on home. Just about the time Preacher got his shoes off, Pornie, the oldest, said, 'I hear Cripple Dick baying at a coon.' Preacher slipped his shoes back on, and the three took off in the direction of Sartin's Mill.

"When they found the dog, he was barking and digging at the end of a hollow log. Preacher ran to one end, Pornie to the other. With a full moon overhead, it was as light as day. Pornie shouted, 'I see him, Pa. I saw his eyes shining like two yellow beads.'

" 'Then don't just stand there,' Preacher said. 'I'll hold him here. You get a fence rail and punch his eye balls out.'

"Leaving the younger son to guard the opening, Pornie dragged up a pole and inserted it into the log. 'It's funny I can't see that varmint,' Preacher said, straining his eyes to see inside the hollow log. 'Are you shore, Por—?' About that time, Pornie lowered the boom. Preacher's voice trailed off, and the younger cried, 'Pornie, you crazy fool, you have gone and killed our pore old Pappy!' "

Fletcher roared with laughter, but Father had found a male Baptist, and he was concerned that he might die before he had a chance to meet him. Breaking into laughter, Father said, "How is this man getting along?"

"Fit as a fiddle now," Jack said.

"You couldn't kill Preacher. He is too tough," Fletcher added.

Relieved, Father brushed off the seat of his pants. "I see my meal is ready. Guess me and the girl here had better be getting back up the trail. I hope you men can see your way clear to attend services Sunday."

"I don't know, Reverend. My rheumatism has been acting up," Fletcher said.

Jack shook his head. "I ain't making any promises. I ain't as young as I used to be."

Again Father put the bag across old Bell's back. The old men had fallen silent under the oak tree. I put an orange sucker into my mouth, and we went next door to the store to get supplies.

Father tied Bell to one of the porch posts, and we went inside. Pausing before a worn, homemade counter, he said, "I'll take a quarter's worth of sugar, Mr. Corbatt."

I inhaled a mixed, uncertain fragrance of candy, raisins, apples, and dried bologna sausage. My mouth watered, and I wished I had another nickel to spend.

The balding Ed Corbatt wiped his hands on his denim apron, lifted a scoop of sugar, and was weighing it on the scales when a salesman came in.

Ed lifted his eyes to greet the fellow. When he did so the paper bag slid sideways, and half the sugar went on the floor. "Now if that isn't a heck of a note. See what you have made me do," Corbatt teased.

I got the feeling the two men had known each other for a long time. The lanky salesman pushed back his cap and grinned good naturedly. "Don't let a little thing like spilling sugar throw you," he said. "You haven't got half the troubles that old farmer whom I stayed with last night has."

Corbatt folded the sugar bag across the top and secured it with twine. "How is that?" he asked.

The salesman's dark eyes grew mischievous. I was intrigued by his carefree manner. "Night caught me over near Low Gap," he said. "Only place in sight was a run-down cabin, and I figured I had better take advantage of it if the people would let me stay. When I pulled up at the gate, I noticed a herd of hogs running like the very devil was after them. An old fellow invited me in, and I took out my team. After supper we moved our conversation to the front porch, and there were those crazy hogs, still running like they didn't have a bit of sense. 'What is ailing those critters?' I asked the man.

"He took a long puff on a pipe that was strong enough to walk. Then he said, 'I don't know what I am going to do about them hogs. They have been like that ever since I came down with a bad cold. There was a few days when I couldn't talk so I would rap against the feed trough instead of calling. I have got my voice back, but they ain't payin' me no mind. They are too busy running down woodpeckers, thinking it is me rapping on that feed trough.' "

Ed Corbatt reached for the broom and began to sweep up the sugar. Half seriously, he said, "You drummers had better be careful telling such whoppers. Mountain folk haven't had much use for the likes of you since Nina Cocks bought that magic churn."

Father had picked up his purchase and seemed ready to go. But at the mention of Nina, he leaned against the counter. My legs were getting a little tired, so I sat on one of the kegs and listened.

Ed leaned his broom against the cracker barrel, and then faced his audience. "One summer a drummer pulled up at the Cocks' place. He unloaded a churn and carried it to the back porch where Nina was shelling peas. 'Lady,' he said, 'I am going to show you one of the greatest inventions since the sewing machine. If you will fetch me some morning milk, I will show you how this churn can cut your butter-making time in half. First of all, there is no waiting for milk to 'turn.' Just strain it into the churn, put in a bit of chemical, and presto, you have butter.'

"Sure enough," Corbatt said, "in the time it took to make his spiel, he made a patty of butter. But Nina already had what she considered the greatest invention, a cream separator. When the drummer realized he wasn't likely to make a sale, he asked about the people on the next farm.

" 'Dodson is the name,' Nina said. 'But I wouldn't go pestering them. Will Dodson was taken in by some sort of salesman not long after he moved here from Georgia. I understand he keeps a gun loaded for the likes of you, so I am warning you for your own good.'

"That devil got a gleam in his eye the minute Nina mentioned Georgia, and he said, 'I would like to make a wager with you. If I can't make a sale with Will Dodson, you get a churn free. On the other hand, if I make the sale, then you buy one at asking price.'

" 'It's a deal,' she cried, triumphant in the belief that he would never make a sale.

" 'Good, I'll just leave the churn, for more than likely you will win the thing,' said the drummer. Then pausing at the edge of the porch, he said, 'You mentioned Georgia. What part of the state are these folks from?'

"This wound Nina up real good. 'They are from Redbank. Will's got a brother who happens to be sheriff of that town. He and his wife, Anna, came out to visit a few years ago. They got an awfully pretty daughter, about your age I would say. Pauline was her name, ain't ever married either.'

"Confident in Will's dislike of salesmen, Nina was still laughing when Ike Cocks came in from the field. Hearing her out, Ike said, 'Wife, you are as crazy as a pet coon, tinkering with something like that. Don't you know them drummers could skin a flea? And they would if there was a market for their hide.'

"About that time, the stranger was turning into Will's yard. Seeing the old man on the porch, he assumed a

chummy attitude. Throwing down his lines, he climbed out
of the wagon and approached Will with a confident smile.
'Howdy friend. Ever hear of Redbank, Georgia?'

"His greeting threw Will off guard. When the salesman
extended his hand, the old man said, 'The wife and I were
born in Redbank. But you know that already. I can see it
in your eyes, young man.'

" 'You are right. I am from the fair city myself. When I
told Sheriff Dodson I was making this trip, he made me
promise to come by, though I must say it was out of my way.
Pauline and Anna send their love.'

"Chubby Will Dodson wiped a tear from his faded eyes.
'Come in, come in,' he cried. 'Dinner is about ready. Come
meet the wife.'

"Later, the salesman feasted on ham, biscuits, and dew-
berry cobbler. But not once did he mention the magic
churns. Will appreciated this. For he had surmised from
the loaded wagon that the guest was some sort of salesman.
When Mrs. Dodson suggested he show some of his products,
the young fellow seemed reluctant. 'I am not one to take
advantage of friendship,' he said. 'But I will tell you this.
Most of the women in Redbank own one of these churns.'

"Whether or not that was true, I can't say," Ed Corbatt
finished. "But I know one thing. Nina Cocks has a magic
churn, bought and paid for, on her back porch." Giving his
friend full attention, he said, "You can see why I am a little
skeptical of the likes of you."

The salesman's eyes took on a new sparkle. "I could
sympathize with you, Ed, really I could; but I happen to
know you merchants have a few tricks of your own."

"Listen to him, Reverend," Corbatt said.

"I am listening," Father joked. "I'd like to know what
you mean by it."

"I am referring to that trick old man Gander pulled a few
years ago." Corbatt brushed this aside.

Father said, "I haven't been here that long. Fill me in."

The sun had climbed overhead; the store was warm and

lazy. The three men slumped on bags of feed, and the drummer began. "Gander has a store up near Jasper. As a publicity stunt to perk up business, he sent out circulars which said, 'Without gadget or mishap one of the Ganders will jump from "lovers leap" next Saturday.'

"Folks came from miles around. Since the excitement wasn't scheduled until five o'clock, the store did a land office business.

"At the appointed time, a hush fell over the crowd waiting at the foot of the bluff. When Mr. Gander appeared, they moved back, giving him plenty of landing room. Word had gotten around that he had a parachute, and the folks wanted to see how it would work.

"But to everyone's surprise, that scamp released a big, fat goose. 'Folks,' he said, 'a gander has jumped.'"

When the men had had their laugh, Father picked up his sugar bag, and we started home. At the door, he paused to say, "Like to see you in church, Mr. Corbatt."

"Nettie has been after me to go," he said. "But after working all week, I like to have some free time for fishing. Be glad to help any way I can though."

"I appreciate that," Father said, turning toward the door, but the salesman stopped him.

He said, "Reverend, you ought to call on old Lidge." Father took a pad and pencil out of his shirt pocket and began to write the directions as the man gave them. "You take Mount Zion road three miles north of the Lacy place. Turn south and follow the creek which will lead you right to his door."

"Lidge used to walk up here to the store every day or so," Ed cut in. "He is a good old fellow. Never used to miss church services when some visiting preacher came by. But he is all crippled up with rheumatism now. Can barely make it to his old friend's house."

"You mean Lidge is still visiting Clint?" the salesman asked.

Nodding, Ed said, "Reverend, you have never seen the

likes of those two. They are the world's best friends, but the bulk of their conversation is taken up in arguing. A few years back when Lidge first got religion, he made an effort not to argue with his friend. Months went by with the two of them coming in here, and no matter what Clint said, Lidge would agree or keep quiet. One day Clint came out with some big spiel. Lidge said, 'I think you are wrong, my friend. But it's your American right to think as you please. After all, we don't all see alike. If we did, this neighborhood would sure be in a dither because every man would want to marry my old woman.'

"Clint almost toppled from his keg. 'You shore made a point that time,' he laughed. 'If everyone saw that old woman the way I do, she would have remained single to her dying day.' "

According to Ed Corbatt, that was the unpardonable insult that started them arguing again.

That evening at the supper table Father looked over his visitation list. Then he told Mother, "Assuming something will come of these prospects, I would say my trip to the mill was quite profitable."

May was the month of lilacs. Between showers, raindrops clung to their fragrant blossoms like so many teardrops.

Since the quilting, I had been taking milk and butter to Millie Lee three times a week. A few days after the trip to the mill Father set out with me. We would leave the milk at the Lee cabin and then find the man called "Preacher."

Winding our way up over a steeper, more direct path than the around-the-mountain road, we could hear late spring in action—in the cackling of our neighbors' hens, in the joyful notes of the mockingbird, and especially in the clanging of the farmer's hammer, as he mended plows, getting ready for a sign that planting should begin.

The old-timers put much stock in the position of the moon and also in the signs of the zodiac when determining the best time for every task. What they knew as "the dark of the moon" was that period when the moon was decreasing. The other half of the lunar season was known as "the light of the moon." Though no one farmer accepted all of the signs, most of them, including Uncle Ben, had a great deal of respect for several. He said:

"Cut your sprouts on the ninth of May,

They will soon be dead, and dead will stay."

Another favorite went like this:

"Sow your turnips the twenty-fifth of July.

Then you will make a crop, wet or dry."

Pondering these sayings as Father and I approached the Lee cabin, I turned to him with a question. "Why shouldn't onions and potatoes be planted on the same side of the garden?"

Father knew that this idea had come from Uncle Ben, and he had no intention of discrediting the old man. But his blue eyes had a twinkle in them when he said, "I imagine the onions would cause the potatoes to cry their eyes out."

Millie had seen us coming and was waiting on the rough, slab porch. She took the milk jug, and we followed her inside where the baby was playing on the floor. Two squares cut in the front logs were too low to let in the sunlight, and the child's golden hair was the only brightness in the single room. Like always when I came, I paused to talk to Ruthie. Although she had a long way to go to achieve normal plumpness, the milk had given her some flesh, and she could stand now.

Millie looked better, too, dressed in a blue checked dress with her long pale hair freshly combed. She offered Father her only chair, a cane-bottom straight-backed. But he declined, saying we had a long trip ahead, a trip he prayed would prove fruitful for the church. "I will be praying for you," Millie said, and we left.

Matching my steps to his, we followed the creek path for a couple of miles. Then we worked our way upward to a gray farmhouse, perched on a narrow mountain ledge. When we reached the top, Father patted a large stone, saying, "Let's get our breath a minute before we raise these folks."

I sat beside him with my hand on his warm knee. Below us lay the hollow with the school, the store, and the millstream.

Father rummaged around in his pants pocket and to my amazement produced four paper shell pecans. "A lady gave these to me yesterday." Placing them in my hand, he said, "They are yours, my sugarplum." While I was cracking and eating, he said, "The old fellows down at the mill were right about Preacher's land being poor. But he sure has himself a view. I would imagine he took all of that into consideration when he settled up here."

Knowing Father's love for people and his desire to shepherd all who would accept his leadership in the church, I had a feeling he was defending Preacher, or at least he was thinking, "This man may not be as crazy as Jack and Fletcher made him sound."

Then he rose, brushed off the seat of his pants, and we made our way up the back way through a barn lot. The outhouse sat alongside the log barn. As we passed between these two buildings, Father pointed out a rambler rose that had overlapped the top of the outhouse, and clusters of scarlet petals were hanging over the other side. Never one to pass up beauty too quickly, Father stopped to appreciate the rose. But a pack of sleeping hounds awakened just then, and they began to bay so loudly and were so close that I could feel the hot breath of one against my leg.

I was glad when a man appeared on the porch. His words frightened me more than the dogs had. "What are you doing on my property?" he boomed.

I had never received this sort of greeting before, but Father answered calmly, and this reassured me. "I am the pastor from Holly Oak Baptist Church," he said. "I understand you are of like faith, so it seemed only fitting that I come to call."

The man's laugh was such that I couldn't decide whether it was friendly or ridiculing. Then he stepped out of the porch shadow, and I looked up and up. He towered almost to the top of the doorframe. His heavy, black hair touched his blue denim collar; and from the top of his head to his big laced-up boots, he was a picture-book version of Paul Bunyan. I wanted to run when he roared, "You understood wrong. I am not a Baptist." Then he added, "Don't know that it makes any difference though. My wife is. Come on in."

On the porch, he offered Father a wire-bottom chair with a soiled cushion. I sat on the top step, still a little uncertain, though our guest seemed friendly enough when he dropped to the porch and leaned back against one of the supports. "So, you heard I was Baptist," he said. By then four long-haired boys had come outside and were staring at me with silent, black eyes.

"That was my understanding," Father said. "But I wouldn't want you to get the idea that I am here to minister to Baptists only. I have a feeling God doesn't always know the difference."

"That's my thinking exactly," said the man. "But the truth is, I am Methodist through and through." Turning his dark eyes on the screenless door, he said, "Come out here, Bonnie. Your pastor's here to see you."

A sprig of a woman in a long, blue, cotton dress appeared, and I had never seen a more opposite couple in all my ten years. As fair as he was dark, she was small and dainty, and her youthful mouth seemed to smile always. Dad got to his feet and extended his hand. When the woman made no effort to take it, he realized that she was blind. I detected a softer note in Father's already gentle voice when he spoke to this childlike woman who was mother to so many big boys. "It's a pleasure to meet you, Mrs.—Mrs.—I am afraid I don't know your last name," he confessed. "The men referred to your husband as Preacher, and I am afraid I forgot to ask."

"Mrs. Horton, pastor. Thank you for coming." Then turning to her husband, she said, "Bring him inside. There is a fresh pot of coffee and some tea cakes."

When Preacher rose, Father got to his feet, and I followed suit. We sat down at a table where the oil cloth had been scrubbed white in the middle, leaving a border of red strawberries. As the men talked, I marveled at the way Mrs. Horton moved around. As surely as if she could see, she filled the black woodstove, then lifted a small cap from the center of a larger one so the coffee could heat next to the flame. Then she set out a platter of chewy molasses cookies. "You dig right in, child," she told me. I needed no second invitation. When I bit into the ginger-flavored treat, I was certain it was the finest cookie I had ever tasted.

She poured coffee for the men. Preacher dunked a cookie, and then he said, "I had heard about services in the schoolhouse. And I was planning to bring the family some Sunday. Then I met with a little accident. One of my boys unintentionally laid me low. Came close to killin' me is what he did." Knowing I remembered the conversation and the laughter at the mill, Father avoided my eyes. "I heard," he said.

"We need some preaching around here," Preacher said. Then he brought up a subject that had been puzzling Father. "Folks calls me 'Preacher' cuz I tried for a time to hold services. There weren't no one else to do it, and Lord knows there needed to be someone on the job with all the moonshinin' and hell raisin' menfolks carries on. It's a shame the way some of the womenfolk suffers, not to mention the children, and all because these hills are full of rotgut liquor. So, I tried to teach the good book the best I knew how. The womenfolk came, but it was a big joke among the men. Bonnie says I got discouraged too easily. Maybe I did. Anyway, it made me realize what problems a real minister has, and you can count on me to stand behind you, pastor. If nothing happens, we will be there Sunday."

We said goodbye then, and there was a new spring in Father's step when we started down the mountain.

We found Paul Holmes' farm in an eighty-acre valley, one mile west of the Horton place. Over the tops of knee-high corn we could see a white house with a latticework railing around the porch and, closer to us, a leaning, gray barn with a man perched on top of the roof, putting on shingles. We had heard the sound of his hammer before we saw the place. When we approached, the man called from the highest point, "Hello there. Be with you in a minute."

I became at ease much more quickly than I had at Preacher's. Father and I watched the man above drive the nails with powerful blows. Paul was naked to the waist, and his muscles stood out with each blow. When he finished, he slid down a dangling rope with all the agility of a circus performer. The second his feet touched the ground, he reached for his shirt with one hand while extending the other in a friendly grasp. "Sorry to keep you waiting," he said. "I put in some hay a couple of days ago, and I felt that I had better get the rest of the shingles on before it rains. It's looking kind of dark back in the west." The day was so bright I had not noticed the gathering storm until Paul Holmes pointed it out.

Father introduced himself as the pastor at Holly Oak. The young man slapped him on the back as though he were greeting an old friend. "Am I happy to meet you," he said. "Yes sir, it's good to hear we will be having services within traveling distance." As he talked, Paul was walking us toward the house. "Deana and I have been churchgoers all of our lives, at least we were until we moved up here. With the nearest church being ten miles away, I'll have to admit we haven't attended the way we would like to." When we reached his neatly painted steps, our new friend said, "Come on in. I want you to meet my wife and our towheaded boys."

In appearance at least, Deana Holmes was the perfect match for her husband. A tall, graceful woman, she had his healthy tan without looking work-worn, and they seemed to laugh every time they looked at each other.

When introductions were over, Deana said, "I have just now put dinner on the table. You folks have got to eat with us." Before Father could object, I heard the clatter of two more plates being placed on the table. Then, "Billy! Denny!" was shouted from the back door. The front screen opened, then closed with a bang, and two live wires, ages six and eight, rushed in.

Later, around an abundant table, Father told the Holmeses about his plans to build a church between the school and the blacksmith shop. "It will take time, and there is a question of money. But there are a lot of good people in these hills, and I'm convinced the Lord will provide. Right now, the problem is men," Father said. "Men who are willing to pitch in and help."

Paul opened his mouth to speak, but his wife's tongue moved more swiftly. "Paul will help," she said. "He can teach, and I'm not bragging but the man can build anything. If you don't believe it, look at our furniture."

I had been looking. A large maple hutch covered half the end of the kitchen. The table and chairs had beautifully carved legs. I had not dreamed they were homemade.

When I looked at my father, his blue eyes were fairly dancing. "This has been a blessed day," he said. "I've been thinking; there are young people in this community that need an enthusiastic couple like you two. I would like to think of you in that teaching capacity. In time there will be money for materials, and Paul will get his chance to build."

"I'm afraid lack of money is holding up a lot of things," Paul laughed. Over coffee he told Father how he had happened to come to the hills. "We had done a lot of camping and fishing in the area. Somewhere along the line, the peace and the beauty of these mountains got a hold on us. One day we decided to stay."

"Our friends thought we had lost our minds," Deana laughed. "Both our parents had cotton land outside of Memphis, but it was sharecropped, and Paul and I had known nothing but the city. Still, we had a feeling about the farm, and this seemed the ideal place to raise kids, cattle, and dogs. Besides, the land was cheap."

"Yeah, mostly the land was cheap," her husband cut in. "After the war, farms were paying off, so I majored in agriculture. Wouldn't you know it, when I got out of school, the bottom had begun to fall out. We had a little money, so we bought this place. We have done alright so far, and I expect to do better."

I helped Deana do the dishes. Then Father said goodbye, and we started home in a slow drizzle of rain.

By the time we reached the creek path the rain was alternating between brisk showers and a steady downpour. But nothing could dampen my father's spirits. He would whistle a little tune; then he would talk about the wonderful people we had met that day. "I just can't wait to tell your mother about that lovely Mrs. Horton," he would say, then almost to himself, "and the Holmes couple, my, oh my, they are just the sort of lay leadership the church has been needing."

We were wet to the skin when we reached home, but I found the state quite refreshing, and I'm sure Father thought very little about it one way or the other. He was too absorbed in the happenings of the day. When he reached our steps, he shouted, "Amy, there is gold in 'them thar' hills."

Mother had been watching for us, and when she opened the screen door, we thought the concern we saw in her eyes was all for the wet clothes. "Smile, Amy," Father teased, "I have got good news."

Mother put a finger across her lips, then said, "Phil Cocks is here. There's been an accident; they need us."

Father was used to postponing his joys for the benefit of others. In a flash he was the concerned shepherd, ready to console a member of his flock. As I followed him to the divan where the boy was sobbing, I knew something bad had happened, for only the worst sort of thing could have made that girl-hating, proud Phil Cocks cry. And he had wept until his sleeve was wet with tears.

"What is the matter?" Father asked.

This brought another flood of tears, "It's Bill," he sobbed. "We found a covey of quails a while ago. We told Papa. He got the gun, and we were going back for them when his pants got caught on the fence he was crossing. Papa sort of stumbled; we boys were behind, and next thing I knew

—Oh dear God, next thing I knew—part of Bill's head was missing."

Mother had told me to go to my room and change my clothes. But Phil had begun his unbelievable story in my presence, and my limbs refused to move. Next to Sybil, I considered Phil and Bill my best friends.

The picture Phil had painted was too terrible for tears. A numbness crept over my body; my head felt light like I might faint. I saw Bob leaning against the doorway, his eyes full of tears. But I couldn't cry. I had a feeling it was all a mistake. I heard Father say, "I'll change my clothes, and then we will go."

I told myself, "We will change our clothes, and we will all go over to Mrs. Cocks. Then we will see it is all a mistake. Bill may be hurt, but he isn't dead; he can't be dead."

Then Mother was leading me into the bedroom. "Hurry, honey," she said. "You children have got to come, too. Ben is off visiting somewhere, and I wouldn't want to leave you here at a time like this."

The rain was still coming down. Father put up the wagon sheet, hitched up the horses, and we drove to the Cocks' place in a silence that was strange for us.

When we pulled up at the sagging, clapboard home, Nina ran out of the house and threw herself into Mother's arms. Her screaming made me face up to reality. This was no mistake. Bill was in there, and he was dead. While mother was comforting Nina, Father went to Ike, a black-bearded man, staring straight ahead on one end of the porch.

When Nina had cried herself out, she led us into the house. There on boards suspended between two chairs, lay my young friend. Some neighboring women had dressed the boy and laid him out the best they could. A sheet was pulled back that I might view the corpse. One side of his face had been discreetly covered. Tears, heartbroken, frightening tears, came when I saw my friend all dressed up in his Sunday pants and shirt. He hated Sunday clothes, and I told myself he would have to wear them forever.

This was my first experience with death, and it was Father's first experience with death as a pastor. So I am sure it was almost as hard on him as it was on Bob and me. Over and over I would hear him ask Mother, "How do you comfort a man that has shot his son?"

But the days passed, and Bill was laid to rest in a small, rocky cemetery where most of the markers were native stones without lettering.

When it was over I tried to forget, but I was beseiged with nightmares. A curtain moving in the night breeze or the pines whispering outside my window would cause my heart to pound, and I would see that sheet and Bill's disfigured face. Added to this trauma was a sudden illness that took Mother and Father away from home for a couple of weeks.

4.
The
Church
Begins
to Grow

The rain had let up in time for the funeral, but it began again the following night. Right after supper, Father complained of a jabbing pain in his right side. A lamp was left burning when we went to bed, a sure sign of sickness at our house. But with Bill on my mind, I wasn't too concerned about my dad until sometime near morning when I heard Mother up and Father groaning in his bed.

Frightened, I crept out from under my covers and tiptoed into my parents' bedroom. Mother, with a worried look on her face, was holding a wash pan while Father heaved. When he fell back against his pillow, he caught sight of my scared face. I had never heard my dad groan before, and it was a terrifying moment. For my sake, he got a firm grip on himself. Trying to smile, he said, "Don't worry, sugarplum, it's only a stomachache. Now go back to bed and try to sleep."

I didn't know that Uncle Ben had gone for Doc Hester, a neighbor who knew enough about medicine to treat minor ailments.

I went back to bed and was pulling the cover up when I

heard the two men come in. Day was breaking by this time. After a bit, I heard Doc Hester say, "Looks like you were right, Ben. I am afraid it is appendicitis."

Bob was awake by now, and when the two of us collided on the way to Father's room, I could tell my brother was as frightened as I was.

"What are we going to do?" Mother's voice quavered.

"There is only one thing we can do," the old doctor whispered. "It's operate or die. We will have to get him to Clarksville." Mother pulled Doc Hester out of Dad's room and voiced the words that were going round in my mind. "An all day ride in the rain? He will die, and you know it."

"It's a risk we will have to take," Ben cut in. "I'll hitch up the horses and put up the wagon sheet. Get some bedding ready. We will get him there as quickly as we can." Ben had his hand on the doorknob when Mother stopped him. "Ed Corbatt has a car. Wouldn't a car be better?"

Ben shook his head. "We couldn't get a car out of here. Mud's hub deep, and the creeks are out of their banks. Now hurry with the bedding and trust the rest to me and the good Lord."

Helpless, Mother went back to the bedroom. When she told Father of Ben's plans, he nodded his head. "I'll be alright," he said. "You look after things and don't worry yourself sick."

"But I am going, too," she said. "The children can ask the neighbors to help, or for that matter, things can look after themselves. I am going with you."

Father rolled his head on the pillow. Between groans, he said, "There is nothing you can do for me. You are needed here to look after the livestock and, more important, the church."

Tears welled up in Mother's eyes, but she didn't argue. The wagon had rumbled up alongside the porch, and Uncle Ben was calling for the bedding. Bob and Doc Hester put a feather bed in the wagon to soften the bumps. Then they carried Father outside. In a downpour, Mother climbed out from under the wagon sheet and, heedless of the rain, gave

Ben some last minute instructions. "Call my dad as soon as you can. He will come from Fort Smith. Let Mother Wilson know; she and Dad will want to know."

"I will," Ben promised. He picked up the lines, and the wagon moved forward. Doc was riding behind with Father, trying to comfort him the best he knew how, and Mother, not quite willing that they go without her, followed them out of the yard. "Take good care of him, and let me hear as soon as possible," she called.

Speechless, Bob and I watched from the porch, and it was the darkest moment we had ever faced when the wagon moved out of sight, taking our father from us. Now we knew the meaning of death, and we were afraid.

Neither of us spoke when Mother came back to the porch, but she cautioned us to listen. "Let's see if they make it across the creek," she said. When the rumbling of the wheels died away, we knew they had overcome the first obstacle. Since we wouldn't know about the other obstacles, we turned sorrowfully inside.

Suddenly, the rooms that had always seemed so full and satisfying were empty without Father and Uncle Ben. In the silence I could hear the tick of our grandfather clock, the steady beat of the rain, a cow mooing in the lot. My ears caught these sounds, but they said nothing to my mind. I was thinking of the times when I had heard someone say, "He died of a ruptured appendix." I had always known appendicitis was a serious illness, but my healthy young mind had refused to think of such things until now. Thinking the worst possible thoughts, I began to tremble, and frightened tears poured down my cheeks. I looked about for comfort, but Bob was biting his lower lip, and Mother was wiping her eyes on an apron she had picked up from the back of a chair.

When it seemed that all courage had flown from our house, Mother spoke, and her voice was full of determination. "Alright now, we have had our cry. Grandpa Tate says tears heal sorrow, and I am inclined to agree because

I feel better already. Let us have a word of silent prayer, and then we'll go on with the chores. Your father would want it that way."

I knew Mother suggested silent prayer, lest we get bogged down with more tears. I bowed my head, and I prayed a childish prayer, full of promises, if only God would let my daddy get well. But he must have heard for a peace came into my heart, and I could tell by Mother's smile that she felt it, too.

"Come on, children," she said. "I will fix us a bite to eat, and then Mary, you can help with the milking while Bob feeds the hogs and the chickens."

After breakfast, we got all bundled up and took our milk buckets out into the gray downpour. The cows were standing with their backs to the rain. When we tried to drive them into the barn, they wouldn't move. Finally Mother put some corn into a basket and led them into the barn. Once they were in the barn, she put the corn away. I knew without being told that until we raised a corn crop, every ounce of grain had to be saved for bread or for the horses. I climbed up into the loft and threw down some hay while Mother was wiping off old Red's dripping udder. As I made my way back down the ladder, I could hear the milk hitting the bottom of the bucket. My clothes were damp to the skin, and I was happy with the idea that we would soon have the chores over and done with. Just then Bob rushed in, all out of breath. "The sow is out," he panted. "I tracked her in the mud, and the crazy, old thing has had pigs between that washout and the creek. Water has backed up in the wash, and the pigs are on a narrow island, an island that is getting smaller all the time."

"Wouldn't you know something like this would happen the first time the men leave," Mother said. Leaving the other cow to milk later, she reached for her corn basket, and we hurried to the disaster area.

At the water's edge, she took off her shoes, and we waded across the knee-deep wash. Mother put the corn basket on the ground and began to call the sow. Bob had brought along a burlap bag. The sow grunted past us and started on the corn as if she knew it would be her last before fall.

"Get the pigs in the bag. Hurry, while I hold her here," Mother said. When I picked up one of the kicking, little porkers, he let out a squeal that brought his mama running. She charged me with her mouth wide open, and I am convinced she would have taken half of my leg if I had not dropped the pig.

"How on earth will we get them out of here?" Mother said, watching the water move closer to the bed.

We tried to get the sow to follow the basket across the water, but she would take a few steps then run back to her babies. Giving up that idea, we tried fighting the sow off while Bob gathered up the piglets. But the black and white beast charged him like a wild boar. "You will have to go to one of the neighbors for help," Mother finally said, and Bob took off in the direction of the Lee cabin.

By now the steady downpour had turned into a water spout, and in a matter of minutes we were soaked to the skin. "We might as well finish the milking," Mother said, knowing it would take three-quarters of an hour to walk to the Lee place and back.

Like two wet chickens seeking shelter, we went back to the barn. Mother finished milking, and we still had some time to wait before we saw Bob coming with Calvin.

Calvin, a lanky, sandy-haired youth, with a mouthful of crooked teeth, had brought a piece of rope with him. Mother grabbed a handful of corn, and we waded back through the wash. The roaring creek had already washed part of the bed away. Calvin looked the situation over, and then he told Mother to put the handful of corn on the ground.

When the sow began to eat, Calvin grabbed her by the hind leg. Around and around they went with man and hog plowing up the mud, but Calvin held on until he had a loop over her foot. Then he wrapped the rope around a persimmon sapling, and the sow couldn't do anything but squeal.

Bob put the six spotted pigs into the basket, and he and Mother carried them to the barn. Then Calvin released the sow. In a fit of anger she swam the stream and was soon nursing her babies in the shelter of the barn.

Calvin helped carry the milk to the house, and on the way home he detoured by way of the store so that he could pass the word about the preacher's illness. Appendicitis was a bad thing in the hill country, and we were soon to learn that mountain folk treated all sickness with the greatest respect. Men stopped by to carry in wood, some offered to do the milking until it faired up a bit, and others came with the womenfolk, in an effort to cheer Mother and keep her mind off of things.

I don't think we could have stood the strain of that day if it had not been for the love and the concern of the people. Sally came as soon as she heard, bringing a small suitcase. "I thought you might like company while the preacher is away," she told Mother. Then she took over the cleaning, the cooking, and the receiving of the visitors who came to keep vigil with us.

All day and far into the night Mother watched the road, hoping for some word. The nearest telephone was six miles away, and three unbridged streams lay between. But sometime after midnight there was a knock. When Mother opened the door, she faced a strange man, clad in a black slicker. "Are you Mrs. Wilson?" he asked.

"I am," Mother said, holding her breath for the worst.

"Ben called," he said. "He says the preacher came through the operation and is doing as well as can be expected. But he doesn't want you to think your husband is out of danger yet. As I understand it, your mother-in-law is with him now, and Ben and the father-in-law are on their way here. Seems you are to go back with the old Mr. Wilson tomorrow."

Relieved, yet still uneasy, Mother invited the man in for some hot coffee. Without argument, he hung his rain slicker across the porch swing and joined the men and women in our living room to await daylight.

Next morning, while we were eating breakfast, Ben drove our wagon into the yard. At the sight of Grandpa Wilson, I forgot to worry and ran coatless out into the rain to meet him. He was a gray replica of my father. A twinkle lit his dark-lashed, blue eyes, and his hug lifted me off the ground.

Bob and I were full of questions, and usually Grandpa was full of talk. But this time we felt that he was eager to eat and be gone.

Soon Uncle Ben came in. "The horses are fed and ready to travel," he said.

We were left with Sally and the old man. In a way, I felt better knowing Mother would be with Father. But I was plagued with bad dreams and all sorts of nighttime imaginings. I needed my parents' reassuring presence like I had never needed it before.

I kept all these things to myself, but I am sure Uncle Ben must have sensed some of my fears, for he spent a lot of time with me, and one had no time for thinking when the old man was around. He filled my days with his best stories, and I particularly remember the day he gave me some lessons in weather forecasting. We had done the morning chores. When Sally went into the house to strain the milk, Uncle Ben and I sat down in the porch swing. The sun had not been up long, and it had given the broken clouds an orange glow. My friend said, "Old folks used to say,
> 'When morning sun is red,
> The ewe and lamb go wet to bed.'

"When the first drops of rain touched the ground and the tips of our noses, we examined them for size, for we were told,
> When drops of rain are big and round,
> They rarely ever wet the ground.

When the raindrops were small, old folks said the reverse was true, and I have to agree, for you'll find,
> When drops of rain are very small,
> The creeks will rise before they fall.

"There was a general belief throughout our community

that early morning showers were of a short duration, and my grandpappy used to say,

> 'Rain before seven,
> Shine before eleven.' "

Uncle Ben also said that rainfall mixed with sunlight meant "the devil was whuppin' his wife." But a rainbow could mean rain or shine, depending on the time of day.

> A rainbow in the morning,
> sailor take warning.
> Rainbow at night,
> sailor's delight.

My friend also told me that between showers when the fog rose rapidly up the mountainsides, leaving the valley as fresh as a mountain spring, we could expect more rain.

> When fog goes up with a hop,
> Rain comes down with a plop.

But if the cloud moved over without fog settling in the valley, then we could expect clear weather.

He said that dampness in table salt and a sun-dog circle around the moon were both promises of rain, as were corn blades curling in the sun and maple leaves turning up to show their silvery undersides. On the other hand, lightning in the south and the crescent moon riding on its back were dry weather signs. Uncle Ben warned me that when these signs prevailed, I could expect the creeks, even our swimming hole, to go dry, for he had seen it happen.

But the signs I found most interesting had to do with animals and fowls.

Uncle Ben said, "All old-timers know that a cock crowing at night is a sure sign of rain. And if a rooster crows during the evening, they say:

> 'A cock crowing when he goes to bed
> Means he'll get up with a wet head.' "

Chickens going to bed earlier than usual or standing around picking themselves instead of hustling for food meant a storm was brewing. But chickens going to bed in the tops of the trees meant that there would be no rain for a while.

When chickens go to roost in
the top of the trees,
No rain in sight for at least a week.

But according to Uncle Ben, one did not have to take the chickens' word for it. Ducks, guineas, and birds could tell anyone as much as chickens could about whether or not there would be rain.

When an unusual quiet prevailed so our neighbor's guineas could be heard "Pot-a-racking" a mile away, rain was in the making. When turkeys turned their backsides to the wind, allowing their feathers to stand on end, there was likely to be some hail. And Uncle Ben said that a flock of crows flying wildly about, cawing and crowing, was a sign of high wind coming.

As might be expected, the call of the rain crow meant rain. But the lonely "whippoorwill," heard first on one hill then another, meant lots of warm sunshine and that it was time to plant cotton.

Crickets chirping more loudly than usual and the squeaky voice of the tree frog were storm warnings, as were an abundance of flies, snakes, and mosquitoes, especially flies if they clung to you like they had " 'lasses" on their feet.

If kingfisher and the bank swallow built their nests near the water's edge, Uncle Ben expected flooding.

He also said that rabbits playing in a dusty road or resting in an unprotected burrow were dry-weather signs. But horses refusing to drink and hogs "toten" sticks for a bed were both signs of rain.

The katydid and the jarfly told us when to expect frost, according to my old friend, and fur-bearing animals told us what sort of winter to expect. "Some vegetables could do as much," he said. To prove his statement, he recited this little rhyme:

"Onion skin mighty thin
Easy winter coming in."

Uncle Ben said that if a squirrel stored more nuts than usual and his fur was extra thick, one should expect a long, hard winter. Strings of geese honking their way south meant cold weather was moving in. "And when you see the family cat turning her backside to the fireplace, you had better believe winter is at the door," he said.

"Now there are several signs of spring," he went on. "One of the best I know is the showing of green on the bodark tree. The return of the turkey buzzard is another, and the return of the killdeer bird is fairly reliable. But the sound of frogs croaking along sky-blue streams and angleworms found near the surface of the warm earth are the best signs that spring has really sprung."

I agreed with my friend that these were good spring signs. But I couldn't help thinking that the frogs, the warm earth, and the worms had meant something else to Phil, Bill, Bob, Sybil, and me. They had meant it was time to take off our shoes, time to do a little wading, and time to go fishing. And we had done just that.

But talking about the weather had been fun, and before I realized it, Father and Mother were back home. Even more wonderful, Grandma and Grandpa Tate came with them for a three-day visit.

This was the first time this set of grandparents had visited our farm, and we children had a hundred things to show them. Grandpa Tate could be both dignified and merry, depending on who was with him. Nearing sixty, he had a close-cropped red mustache; and his red hair, as yet untouched with gray, made him look considerably younger than his years. His crisp suits and his well-scrubbed hands were in sharp contrast to Grandpa Wilson's overalls and work-worn nails. But both men had a special place in my heart, and it gave me a nice warm feeling having Grandpa Tate and my talkative, fluttery little grandmother in our house. Meanwhile, Father's incision was healing nicely. After three days, Grandma and Grandpa Tate packed their automobile for the trip back to Fort Smith.

Paul Holmes conducted church services the two Sundays Father was convalescing. He did such a fine job, Father jokingly said, "I wouldn't dare stay away any longer. I might lose my job."

As Father had hoped, the Holmes couple proved to be the kind of leadership the church needed, especially in the youth department. To arouse interest, they planned all sorts of outings that appealed to the youth of the community. Considering that entertainment had to be invented and the nearest town was miles away, it was little wonder that the back desks of the school-church were soon overflowing.

Another thing which made Deana and Paul Holmes so popular was the fact that they owned a beautiful Victrola and a large record collection.

One of their first socials was a 4th of July, church-wide get-together to help everyone get better acquainted. From the pulpit, Father announced an ice cream feast, going on to say, "While the men are turning the freezers, there will be ball games, sack racing, and lots of music for the young folk."

Father was counting on the ice cream and the Victrola to bring a lot of new people. But he was unprepared for the crowd that met his eyes when we pulled up at the Holmes's farm. It looked as though every wagon in the hills had found its way to Paul's valley. The newly cut meadow was full of children. Some were playing baseball, some were racing, and the rest were milling around, enjoying the company of others without doing anything. The women had brought large baskets of fried chicken, potato salad, and chocolate cakes. These ladies, wearing Ozark sunbonnets, were busy around a large plank table set in the shade of an American elm.

Old-timers were swapping tales under a yard oak, and the younger men were turning lard buckets in tubs of ice, the mountain way of making ice cream when one didn't own a freezer.

Music poured from the house, and when Uncle Ben stopped the horses, I could see young people milling around the "front room" windows. "Isn't this some turnout?" Father said.

Uncle Ben declared it was the best he had seen since he was a young man. "Ice cream did it," he said. "Folks don't pass up ice cream if they can help it."

Bob jumped off the wagon before it came to a halt and ran to join some boys in the meadow. Mother carried her basket of food to the table, and Father took his turn at one of the freezers.

I looked around for Sybil. When I didn't see her, I followed Uncle Ben to the front porch. He sat down on one of the steps where he could hear the music without intruding on the young folk.

"I been wantin' to hear some of that new fandangle music," he told me. At that moment the bright sunlit day was filled with, "Jota, jota, jota, jota, jing, jing, jing."

Uncle Ben stirred uncomfortably. "I hope the next one is more lively and that it will make a bit more sense. I like ballads, good, old-time songs that tell a story," he said.

The jota record came to an end, and I heard someone winding up the machine. The needle was set in place, and a high pitched voice sang, "I told every little star. . . ."

I found the song breathtaking in a romantic way, but when I glanced in Uncle Ben's direction, his rosy face had a disappointed expression. Shaking his head, he said, "They don't write pretty songs like they did when I was a lad."

Later, when everyone was full of good food, some of the men brought out their instruments for some of Uncle Ben's kind of music. Though the old folks called them ballads from their day, most of the songs they sang had been written many years before they were born.

According to Randolph Vance, an authority on Ozark songs, "She Wore the Waterfall," was written before 1860 because that hair style was not popular after that time. But in the hills it was still played at picnics and other gatherings. It went like this:

> Come all you young people,
> And sympathize with me.
> For I have loved the fairest maid,

That ever I did see.
Her age was scarcely seventeen,
Her figure fair and tall.
Oh, such a handsome creature,
She wore the waterfall.

The first time that I saw her,
I never shall forget.
I stepped into a drygoods store,
Some handkerchiefs to get.
She stood behind the counter,
All dressed up like a doll,
And such a handsome creature,
She wore the waterfall.

The next time that I met her,
I never shall forget,
It was a picnic party,
And we began to chat.
Although many girls were there,
None of them at all
Could dance with me
Except the girl that wore the waterfall.

I asked to see her home that night,
I swore we would never part,
And when she asked me to come in,
I thought I had won her heart.
We hadn't been sitting there very long
When I heard footsteps in the hall.
All sorts of colors turned this girl,
That wore the waterfall.

Before I could say goodnight,
A fellow came stalking into the room.
And when he saw me sitting there,
He began to fume.

His hair was red,
His words were rash.
My love it did depart.
This is my husband,
Said the girl
That wore the waterfall.

Once more I tried to say goodnight,
But he beat me across the room.
And while this maiden held me down,
He beat me black and blue.
When I got up I found I had lost,
Watch, money, change and all.
I have never since that day been near,
The girl that wore the waterfall.

"The Two Orphans" came next. In spite of its sad story,
children enjoyed singing this one.

Two little orphans, a boy and a girl,
Sat by an old church door.
The little girl's face was as brown as the curl
That lay on the dress that she wore.

Her dress was faded and hatless her head.
A tear shown in each little eye.
"Why don't you run home to your mama?" I said,
And this little maiden replied.

"Mama's in heaven; God took her away.
Left Jimmie and I all alone."
Then she stepped up to the boatman and said,
"Please row us over the tide."

"We are too little to earn our bread,
I am five, and Jim's only seven.

We came here to rest at the close of the day,
For our own dear mama's in heaven."

Mama told little Jimmie one day,
That God would take care of her child.
But there isn't room in heaven today,
So row us over the tide.

The Sexton came early to ring the church bell
And found them beneath the snow white.
The angels had made room for the orphans to dwell
In heaven with Mama that night.

Uncle Ben liked to sing, "His Old Beard a'Hanging."

My mama told me to open the gate.
Oh, but I won't have him.
I opened the gate; he walked so straight,
With his old beard a'hanging, old beard a'hanging.

My mama told me to open the door.
Oh, but I won't have him.
I opened the door; he fell on the floor,
With his old beard a'hanging, old beard a'hanging.

My mama told me to carry his valise.
Oh, but I won't have him.
I carried his valise; he fell in some grease,
With his old beard a'hanging, old beard a'hanging.

My mama told me to get him a drink.
Oh, but I won't have him.
I got him a drink; he fell in the sink,
With his old beard a'hanging, old beard a'hanging.

My mama told me to put him to bed.

Oh, but I won't have him.
I put him to bed; he covered his head,
With his old beard a'hanging, old beard a'hanging.

But children preferred "Sweet William," and "Where Are You Going My Pretty Miss?" Both are eighteenth-century English ditties.

I love sweet William,
I do, I do.
I love sweet William,
So hee haw haw.
I love sweet William,
But don't you tell Pa
For he will whup me,
And you know it, my ma.

We are going to be married,
We are, we are.
We are going to be married,
So hee haw haw.
We are going to be married,
But don't you tell Pa,
For he will whup me,
And you know it, my ma.

Oh now we are married,
We are, we are.
Oh now we are married,
So hee haw haw.
Oh now we are married,
But don't you tell Pa,
For he will whup me,
And you know it, my ma.

We fuss and we fight,
We do, we do.

We fuss and we fight,
So hee haw haw.
We fuss and we fight,
But don't you tell Pa,
For he would whup me,
And you know it, my ma.

We have three children,
We do, we do.
We have three children,
So hee haw haw.
We have three children,
But don't you tell Pa,
For he will whup me,
And you know it, my ma.

Finally the banjos and the fiddles were put aside. A full moon rose in the east, making silver patterns around the front porch. In such a setting no wonder someone suggested love stories of bygone days. When no one volunteered right away, one of Uncle Ben's great-nephews said, "I would like to hear how Uncle Ben met Aunt Ollie." I was sitting near my old friend. I felt him stir, a bit embarrassed. Then his eyes took on a faraway look; and the next moment I was hearing a side of his life that I had never heard before.

"Blue-eyed, red-headed Ollie Hobbs was one of the most beautiful girls in Newton County. I think most of you old-timers will agree to that," Ben said.

A murmur of agreement rippled through the group, and Uncle Ben continued, "But man-o-live, that girl had a temper, and it took her wrath to tame a rascal like me.

"When Ollie turned seventeen one May, her brother Sam came back across the hills to work in a sawmill near my home. A few weeks later, he met my sister, Lacy; and the two of them ran off and got married. Sam took Lacy home with him. When I found out, I was ready to be tied, for I had forbidden Lacy to see him.

"Lacy and Ollie were about the same age, and the two

girls loved each other from the moment they met. Naturally, Lacy told Ollie about my threat, that I would kill Sam if he didn't leave my sister alone. 'Why would he want to do that?' Ollie asked. 'Sam is a good boy, and he loves you.'

" 'I know,' Lacy said. 'But Ben has looked after me since Ma and Pa died. He thinks I am still a youngun' and that I can't possibly know my own mind.'

"Ollie tried to console Lacy with the idea that my bark was probably worse than my bite, but the truth was, she was afraid for Sam, too.

"But nothing could dampen Ollie's spirit for long. A few mornings later when she awoke and was still lying in her bed with everyone else asleep, she realized it was the first day of May, the day when a girl was supposed to be able to see her future husband by walking to the well backwards. She had been told that a face would appear on the surface of the water, and by looking into a mirror, she could see her intended.

"Just for the heck of it Ollie jumped out of bed, pulled on an old cotton smock, and headed for the well with her pa's old looking glass.

"When she reached the curbing, it occurred to her that she might see a coffin instead of the reflection of her future husband—and in that case, she would die before she wed. But as some of you will remember, Ollie had more guts than gumption. So she leaned over backwards and held up the mirror.

"Now I am ashamed to say so," Uncle Ben said, "but I had come gunning for Sam, and I had spent the night in Mr. Hobbs' barn. When I saw Ollie at the well, I eased up behind her, and she caught my reflection in her looking glass. 'I hadn't really expected to see anything,' she told me later, 'and when the face of a man did appear, it nearly scared me to death.'

"She dropped the mirror and started to run, but I caught her by the shoulder and swung her around to face me. She only came to my shoulder but I had tangled with a wildcat.

She kicked me on the shins, and she shouted. 'According to that lookin' glass, you are the man I am supposed to marry. But I would "druther" be dead than married to a no-good bum that goes gunning for his sister's husband.' Before I realized it, she yanked the gun from my hands and threw it down the well.

"Well, the truth is, I had changed my mind about a lot of things the moment I saw Ollie looking so young and innocent. For the first time in my life, I was tongue-tied in the presence of a pretty girl. Not only was Ollie's beauty completely disarming, but also her temper was an element I had not seen in another girl.

"When she had calmed down enough to listen, I asked if I might come in and apologize to Sam. She agreed, but she kept out of my sight. She wouldn't even have breakfast with me and the family. But she had met someone as determined as herself. When I told her I wouldn't leave until she promised to marry me, she decided she might fight love but she could not fight fate that had reflected my face in her pa's old looking glass."

Uncle Ben's reminiscing brought a round of laughter. But I had an even greater respect for him, for I had never dreamed that he was such a swashbuckling figure in his youth. I was trying to imagine him as young and in love when Nettie Corbatt said, "In olden times, in the month of May girls went out to look for bird nests. The number of eggs in a nest represented the number of children one would have, and the number of birds was an indication of the years before one would wed. But the more poetic way was to look over the left shoulder and recite this poem:

> May moon, May moon,
> Round and fair,
> Under my left foot
> I'll find a hair.

By some stroke of May-time magic, the girl was supposed to find a hair from the head of her future husband. But no girl was likely to be satisfied with a mere hair—so next time she saw a new moon, she could look over her right shoulder and recite another poem that would tell her a good deal more in a dream. It went like this:

New moon, new moon, do tell me,
Who my own true love will be.
The color of his hair,
The color of his eyes,
And the happy, happy day
We two shall meet."

Sally said, "I have heard it said a girl can count nine stars for nine consecutive nights and then go to bed and dream of the man she will wed. But I haven't tried it yet."

A perky little lady whom I suspected of having been an impatient lass said the same could be accomplished by winking at a star twice.

Fletcher Kindrick said there were love potions for boys, too. But as I listened, I decided they weren't very effective, for most of the male stories had hectic endings to say the least.

For instance, there was the bashful boy who fell in love with a high-filutin girl. Not trusting his own powers as a lover, he burned salt in the fireplace for three consecutive nights while repeating these words:

It's not salt I wish to burn,
But my own true love's heart to turn.
Wishing her neither joy nor sleep,
Till she is mine and mine to keep.

According to Fletcher, the boy went calling then and made such a hit with the girl's parents, they invited him to spend the night and go to church with them the following day. The boy agreed, and since he had walked a long way over a dusty road, he thought he ought to wash his feet. There were no bathrooms in Ozark country, and come bedtime, he washed his feet in the wash pan. Then thinking he was opening an outside door, he threw the water onto a sleeping porch, and it landed on the bed where the girl was sleeping with her mother. Though both women assured him that no harm had been done, he was so miserable he scarcely slept.

When morning came and the youth was called to breakfast, he was as nervous as a heifer being milked for the first time. After the blessing was said, the man passed the biscuits. The boy started to take one, but it rolled to the floor. He stooped to pick it up, and at that moment the girl passed him a bowl of hot gravy. His nose landed right in the middle of it. By this time, the boy had taken all he could stand. Fleeing the kitchen, he walked home, and he never called on that girl again.

Thus far, Father had listened and laughed with the rest of us. But remembering his moment of popularity at the mill, the first time there was a lull in the conversation, he said, "That reminds me of an old boy my dad knew down in Tennessee. The young fellow had been forbidden to see his girl, so he would wait until her parents drove by his cabin. Then he would call on her while they were away. One night after they left for church, he went calling. Well, they got so wrapped up in each other, he forgot the old man until he heard footsteps on the porch. The boy had taken off his shoes, and before he could grab them, the girl pushed him up the stairs to an attic bedroom. She planned to let him out of the house as soon as her dad went to bed, but the old man decided to have a bedtime snack.

"The fire on the hearth burned low, and the boy's bare feet got cold. Finally he noticed a sheepskin rug on one side of the room, and he decided to go stand on that. He tiptoed across the attic and stepped into the middle of the skin. Next thing he knew he had landed on top of the kitchen table! The rug had been used as a covering over a hole where an old flue had been torn out.

"The startled dad grabbed the lad by the seat of the pants and threw him out the back door. After that, the girl was afraid even to look at the youth," Father said.

Fletcher said laughingly, "The young man might have made out better had he made a necklace of paw-paw seed, or he might have hidden a turtle dove tongue on his person, but I wouldn't guarantee either one. But I have heard it said that a lover's quarrel can be mended by setting one's shoes in a certain way and reciting this little poem:

> When my true love I long to see,
> I set my shoes so they form a T."

When the young folks had had their laugh, he said, "Better still, recite:

> Stump your toe,
> Kiss your thumb,
> See your love
> 'fore bedtime comes."

During our nonsense fun, the moon had climbed high into the sky. Father said, "Speaking of bedtime, I would say it is about that time. I imagine we had better get things loaded and be on our way."

Everyone agreed, and when we were climbing into our wagon, Father felt a tug at his sleeve. Turning, he faced a sad-eyed woman, who had been introduced to him as Mollie Hagerton. "Reverend," she said, "I want you to know I would attend your church if I had a way to get there. I am a widow, and I live in an out-of-the-way place. There is no one I know of going that way on Sunday mornings."

"Do you live alone?" Father asked.

"No, my son, Jim, lives with me; that is, he lives with me what time he isn't away working. I wanted to speak to you about him," she said. "I wish you would talk to him. Maybe you could get him interested in the good book. Jim is a smart boy. Sometimes I think he is too smart. He wants to make something of himself. But there is nothing for him in these hills. I have been sickly for years, and he feels duty bound to look after me. I am afraid—"

Her words trailed off on "afraid," and Father sensed a real concern in the mother. He promised to visit the youth the following day and, also, to find her a ride to church.

On the way home Father kept thinking about the young man. For one thing, he had seen the way boredom and few opportunities had turned some of the finest youth to drink and to all sorts of hell raising.

As the wagon bumped along the moonlit path called a road, Father said to Uncle Ben, "How well do you know Jim Hagerton?"

Uncle Ben clicked the lines, urging the horses forward. Then he said, "I know he is one of the cussingest, fightingest, hardest working young fellows you are likely to meet. He's a handsome cuss. Girls are all crazy about him. Even Sally was sweet on him. Why do you want to know?" When Father told of his conversation with the mother, Ben shook his head. "I am afeared he won't listen to you. He is a likable young man, but he is set in his ways—and most of his ways are bad."

Father dropped the subject, or else I fell asleep in the back of the wagon. But later when I was cozy in my own bed, I heard him mention Jim Hagerton's name in prayer.

Father was a firm believer in answered prayer. The next morning while we were having breakfast, Uncle Ben said, "Speak of the devil, and he is bound to show up." Pointing out the window, he said, "That young feller coming down the Lee cabin trail is your Jim Hagerton. It would save you a long trip if you could find the opportunity to talk to him down at the store."

Father gulped down his coffee, put his hat on his head, and took off behind the youth.

5.
Problems
and
Growing
Pains

At the store, Father asked about Jim. Ed pointed toward the blacksmith shop. "I saw him go in over there a few minutes ago," he said.

Several men perched on the nail kegs paused to listen when Father mentioned Jim's name. Backing up what Uncle Ben had said, Fletcher Kindrick claimed the youth could out-shoot, out-cuss, out-fish, and out-saw anyone in the hills.

"Personally, I have always felt sorry for that young fellow," Ed said. "His dad died when he was ten or thereabout. Jim went to work soon afterwards. He had a sick mother and a couple of sisters to provide for. Logging is heavy work for a man, but that youngun' kept up with the best of them. He felt that he had to."

Fletcher Kindrick was warming one of the kegs, and he broke into the conversation to say, "He could drink with the best of them, too. By the time he was fifteen, he spent most Saturday nights brawling. I dare say Hagerton has broken more noses than any man I know."

"Too bad he couldn't have gone on to school and made something of himself," Ed continued in a different vein.

"My sister taught him all the book-learning he has had. Taught him in a little school near his ma's farm. Don't think he got past fourth grade, but she always said Jim Hagerton was as sharp as a tack."

"That may be," Fletcher said, "but he has cut himself a bad record, and one of these days the law will get him, or he will get himself killed. Watch what I tell you." Father left the men and made his way to the youth they were still discussing.

He found Jim Hagerton leaning with indolent ease against the side of the blacksmith shop. One foot was drawn up behind him, with the sole of his foot propped against the gray boards of the building. Slender hands were tucked in the rear pockets of his jeans, and a black, cotton shirt fit his torso snugly, emphasizing the breadth of his shoulders. A western hat was pulled low on his forehead, all but hiding his piercing blue eyes, and the shadow from the brim softened the taut lines of his deeply tanned face.

As Father approached, he saw the youth was lost in thoughts of his own, thoughts that gave him a faraway look and a half smile. Sizing him up, Father recalled Uncle Ben's statement, "Girls are crazy about him," and he could see how a young woman might find Jim Hagerton attractive, but he was already convinced that the rough and tough side of the youth had been exaggerated. When Father paused beside him, he saw a muscle twitch at the corner of Jim's mouth, but like a cat pretending indifference, the youth stared straight ahead.

In his brightest voice, Father said, "Hello, Jim. I am the pastor here at Holly Oak. I met your mother yesterday; she promised to come to Sunday school, and I am hoping you can come, too."

As Father talked, the young man shot to attention, and his tight mouth seemed to say, "How dare you speak to me about such things?" When the lips parted, Father got a firm grip on himself for the storm that was certain to follow. But to Father's surprise, Jim's fury turned to ridicule; he roared with laughter, a deep, mocking laughter that echoed back from the hills beyond.

Father stood his ground, patiently waiting until Jim had laughed out his little joke; and the fact that the preacher seemed unperturbed angered the young man all the more. "Preacher," he hissed, "you want me to tell you what I think of your church and everyone in this Godforsaken valley?"

"I wish you would," Father said. "Maybe it's something I need to know, something that needs correcting."

Like a deflated tire, Jim fell back against the building. With his eyes on the ground, he said, "Fat chance you will have correcting that bunch of hypocrites. But who am I to talk? I am no good either. You are wasting your time on the rotten lot of us."

The desperation in his words gave Father hope. "Friend," he said, "when a man recognizes his own unworthiness, there is hope for him. Besides, the Bible agrees with you—we are a rotten lot. Yes, even me. The Scripture says 'All have sinned.' 'There are none righteous, no not one.' So your observations of human nature are more or less correct. But there is hope through Christ. I believe that, and that is why I am here."

For an instant a boyish softness lit Jim's eyes, but then he glanced across the road, and the old hardness returned. "I have got nothing against you," he said. "But hell raising is part of my reputation. Folks like it that way; they have encouraged it in me since I was a child. It is part of the excitement they enjoy, because they haven't the brains to enjoy anything better."

Father shook his head. Jim said, "So you don't believe me. Well, take a look across the road, all of 'em gathered on the store porch, eyeballs big as apples, hoping Jim Hagerton will black the preacher's eyes. Given a little whiskey, I might have done just that. I go crazy as h— when I drink, but sober, I am not so d— bad."

Father glanced toward the store. Sure enough, five men were poking each other and laughing as though they had witnessed the best joke of the year. Disgusted, he said, "Come on, give them something to wonder about. I need a strong man to help me set the school in order for church service."

A grin played around the corner of Jim's mouth. He took a step forward, then fell back against the wall. "Sorry, Preacher. I almost forgot. I am meeting a fellow here. He is giving me a job. One day, he will take me out of this Godforsaken place."

Disappointed, Father walked back to the store. A few minutes later two men drove up in one of the finest cars he had ever seen. As it paused near the blacksmith shop, Jim Hagerton climbed into the back seat, and the car roared away.

At the noon meal, Father tried to describe the car to us. "It was brown and tan with the largest chrome headlights I have ever seen," he said. "The inside was all brown leather, and the two well-dressed men who were in the car were smoking big cigars."

"There is no one in these parts like that," Uncle Ben said. "Who do you think they were?"

Father shook his head. "I have no idea."

"Well, I will tell you one thing, they won't go far in that big car once the winter sets in. It will sink right down to the hub caps," Uncle Ben said.

We weren't the only folk pondering the new people. At church, the store, everywhere we went, there was a new story about the strangers and their fine new car. Ed Corbatt told how two women had driven it to the store for groceries. Winking at Father, he spoke to the tobacco-chewing crew seeking warmth from his stove now that frost had driven them inside. "You really missed a show," he said. "One of the gals had sort of yellow hair, done in little bitty curls. The other woman had black hair with a wide band around her head. Both women wore spike heels, plenty of perfume; and they were smoking cigarettes in long holders."

Nettie exchanged glances with some of the other women, a glance that clearly said, "You know what they are." Nettie had never seen any other kind of woman smoking cigarettes. Neither had Nina Cocks, and she nodded knowingly. So the stories circulated, and one day when Uncle Ben came home from the mill, he said, "I hear them city fellers are brothers. Mike and Joe Parson, I think the names were. The women Ed told about are their wives. Seems these men have inherited a lot of money. I can't figure out why they would come here, but I guess they are here to stay. I am told they bought the farm in back of us."

A mountain and a lot of bluffs lay between our house and the Parsons' farm. But as the crow flew, they were our nearest neighbors; and Father, doing his pastorial duties, went calling.

He found the weeds and the brush had been cut away from the run-down house and barn, giving the place a halfway lived-in look. But it seemed incongruous with the clothing, the fat cigars, and the car. As he neared the barn, he found Jim Hagerton mending fence, and the young man pointed out some thoroughbred horses that had been turned into the pasture. "I am to take care of these horses, do some cleaning up, and run errands for the folks. Not bad for the salary I am getting," he told Father.

Father wished him well in his work and went on to the house.

The blond woman met him at the door. "The men aren't home," she said. But when Father introduced himself, she invited him in.

The dark sister-in-law brought a tray of cookies and some small cracker sandwiches. As the women fluttered about, talking in their crisp, northern way, Father learned they were from Chicago. Their nightclub had failed, but they had inherited enough money to live comfortably. "We are going to turn this old house into a show place," blond Mrs. Joe Parson said. Father wasn't certain which way she meant her words. His eyes took in the sparse furnishings and the newspapered walls. But another question was burning in his mind. "Where did you meet Jim Hagerton?" he asked.

"Mike met him at one of the sawmills," the dark woman said. "The men came through here a few weeks back looking for a place to rent or buy. Jim seemed so bright and so discontented with his job, Mike felt that he deserved something better."

Father invited the new people to church, doubting they would come. But the following Sunday, while he was making the announcements, an uncertain, though lovely fragrance drifted up the aisle. The school door closed with a bang, and the two women with glittering earlobes and sparkling fingers followed their polished husbands toward the front.

Father preached hard that day but I doubt anyone heard, for all thoughts were on those beautiful people. *Who are they?* I wondered. What would it be like to be rich? To own jewels, cars, and horses? My mind leaped over the mountains, and I saw ladies in furs, dangling earrings, and long gloves. They shopped in stores ten times the size of Corbatt's. They bought the biggest apples, the largest peppermint sticks, and a tub of ice cream. My mouth watered, and I wished Father were rich. But he wasn't, and the next thing I knew he was saying the benediction.

Still a little dazed from all of my dreaming, I watched the congregation surge forward. One by one, the homespun souls, under guise of Christian greeting, went forward to look upon the rich newcomers.

Later, when everyone had cleared out of the building, Paul Holmes shoved the offering plate in front of Father. He said, "This is one Sunday the pastor gets paid." Wondering what had brought about that unheard-of remark, Father's eyes fell upon the usual change and two twenty-dollar bills.

Handing the bills to Father, Paul said, "The Parsons' donation. It's hard to tell when we will see that much money again. You have been here going on a year; I would say you deserve that forty dollars."

My heart raced at the idea of so much money. Drought had hit our cotton in June after too much rain in May. The half-opened bolls would not produce that much money. But a questioning frown had creased Father's brow. Shaking his head, he said, "Put it in the building fund. Maybe the Lord has sent them to help us build a church."

It did seem so, for the people continued to worship with us, not regularly, but often. And each time they came, they gave a large offering.

Winter came and went, and the Parsons made another contribution to the neighborhood. Almost from the beginning of the Parsons' residence in the mountains, Jim Hagerton's mode of living had changed. No longer a brawler, he dressed in the latest fashions, and he drove up and down the dusty road in a two-seat sports coupe, which his employers had purchased just for him. Jim brought his mother to church most Sundays. Though he never stayed for services, he picked her up afterwards, and he and Father were friends of a sort. Father was an amateur archaeologist, and so was Jim. Some years back, the university had given Father credit for discovering two major Indian sites. When Jim heard about this, he began to drop by the house. The two men would talk Indians, or else they would take a look at some place where Jim had discovered some arrowheads. Church wasn't mentioned during these visits, but Father hoped to win him through this interest.

One spring day when Jim came to call, he said, "Calvin Lee has gone to work for the Parsons. There is more work than I can handle with the horses, the decorating, and the hundred or so things they have got going on around there."

When Millie and the baby came to church looking well fed and neatly clothed, Father thanked God for the Parson money and the contributions it was making to our community. But there were times when it troubled him. Too many things didn't add up. For instance, with two hired hands the place still had a run-down look. Since their coming, we had had a steady stream of traffic past our place, and more than one had seemed to be intoxicated. Finally, a number of women came to Father, complaining that their husbands were getting whiskey somewhere; they suspected the Parson brothers of bootlegging. One woman said, "I think they are making their rounds at the sawmills every pay day, because my man comes home without a dime every Monday evening. Mind you, I don't see him all weekend. And it is happening in many homes, even though we barely get along at best."

Father promised to keep his eyes open and, should he find some proof that they were conducting an illegal business, to call the law.

A few days later, one of our cows got out. When Father followed her tracks along a bluff on the Parson land, he came upon their whiskey-making operation. He herded the cow back toward the house, hoping he had not been seen. But when he reached the fence that separated our farm from the Parsons' farm, he saw Joe galloping toward him on one of his shiny black horses. Smiling around his cigar, Joe said, "I like you, Preacher. For one thing, you strike me as having more sense than some of these yokels."

Without comment, Father nailed the broken fence back to the post. When Father turned to go, Joe leaned down from his saddle; he tapped Father on the shoulder. "Forget what you have seen, and I'll build that church for you," he said.

Looking him squarely in the eye, Father said, "You won't build anything for me. And every cent you have contributed will be returned no later than tomorrow." With that, he walked away, leaving Joe with an angry look on his face.

Hoping to warn Millie Lee of the trouble that was brewing and, if possible, to clear Calvin, Father turned the cow into the lot, gave Mother a swift rundown of his plans, and took off.

He had been gone about a half an hour when the brown and tan car stopped at our gate. Mike threw a sawed-off shotgun across his shoulder. Mother and I with hearts hammering in our chests saw them stomping up our steps. "Where is the preacher?" Joe asked when Mother opened the door.

"I don't know," she lied. "He went after the cow. I haven't seen him. Have you, Mary?" I shook my head, unable to speak. Shoving past us, the two men looked in all of the rooms and, satisfied Father wasn't there, went back to the car. Just then, Uncle Ben came around the barn, and they asked him about Father. Not knowing what had happened, he said, "I saw him take off toward the Lee place a few minutes ago."

The men jumped into the car and roared off in a cloud of dust.

"Stay here," Mother said. "I am going to try to warn your daddy before they get there." She took off in a run, over a path that was about half the distance the men would have to travel by car. I started to run after her, but then I turned back to tell Uncle Ben. "The—Parsons—" I panted. "They—are going to kill Daddy."

The old man threw down his plow, ran for his double-barreled shotgun, and took off after Mother. When I tried to follow, he repeated Mother's words, "Stay here." But Bob had gone to the store, and I wasn't about to stay there alone. With heart pounding, I kept a safe distance behind him, thankful that he didn't look back.

The car beat Mother there by a few seconds. When we arrived, Joe Parson had his gun pointed at Father's stomach. Between all sorts of swear words, he said, "I am warning you, preacher, one word to the law, and I will blow you to God Almighty." I was so scared I was shaking like I had a hard chill. Since Father had no weapon, my only hope lay in the fact that Uncle Ben had been a sharp-shooter in his day, according to the story I had heard the night of the picnic. And my old friend didn't fail me. I heard him say, "If you don't want both of these barrels going off in your belly, you had better get back in that fancy car and get on your way."

Pressing my hand to my lips to keep from screaming, I watched the gun fall from its perch on Father's belt. Without a word, the men walked back to the car. Just before they roared away, Mike said over his shoulder, "We aren't done with you yet. You will be sorry, mighty sorry."

Father must have been frightened. But he showed no sign of fear. He was much too busy trying to comfort Mother and poor Millie. "They will kill you," Mother was weeping, and Millie was crying, "Oh, what has Calvin gotten himself into?"

This took place on a Wednesday. We took Millie and the baby home with us. That night when we were returning from prayer meeting, Uncle Ben happened to look back. "Lord-a-mercy," he said, "the school is on fire!" He turned the wagon around, and we raced to the scene, but everything went up in smoke.

Soon the valley was full of people coming to help, to look, to shake their heads and wonder how such a thing could happen.

When we reached home, we found our house all topsy-turvy from the front room to the basement. There was no doubt in our minds now. Mike and Joe Parson had burned the school, and they had done this to us. While we were pondering what we ought to do, someone knocked at the door.

"Don't open it," Mother pleaded with Father.

When he hesitated, a voice whispered, "It's me, Preacher; it's Jim Hagerton. I want to help you."

"It's alright if it's Jim," Father said.

Mother wasn't so sure, but the young man was let in. He stared around him in disbelief. "They did this!" He gritted his teeth, and a cussword escaped before he realized where he was. "They dared break in here after they burned the school! Preacher," he said, "I am guilty of bootlegging, I admit that. But I never dreamed I was working with men so low that they would try to destroy my community."

Without reproach, Father said, "Maybe it's a lesson you had to learn, Jim."

We were still huddled around the door, all of us looking at Jim, wondering what would come next. Wearily, he dropped to a chair. "I have learned my lesson," he said, "but it has come a mite too late. The law will be here in a few minutes. I turned those rotten sons of a cur in. Leastwise, I sent Ed Corbatt for the sheriff. They'll arrest the Parson brothers and then come for me. I told Ed I would wait here."

"What about Calvin?" Father asked. Millie had gone home when we left for prayer meeting, hoping to hear from her husband. "He is in it, too," Jim said. "Calvin operated the still. I delivered to the sawmills."

"I will help you any way I can," Father said. Then we waited for some word or indication that the Parson men had been arrested.

Shortly before midnight, Ed knocked at our door. When Father invited him in, he said, "Everything is alright, Reverend. We have part of the gang in my car, part in the sheriff's."

"Calvin too?" Father asked.

"Calvin too," he repeated. "Better let his wife know."

Father nodded. Jim got to his feet, and I got a lump in my throat when I saw the look of grief on Father's face. His young friend followed Ed out to the car. Dad closed the door, but not his heart.

The next few days were hard ones for Father. In addition to having no church or school, a lot of unfounded tales began to circulate. One day Ben came home from the store ready to be tied. We were chopping cotton in the apple orchard when he joined us. Wiping the angry sweat from his brow, he said, "That low-down Fletcher Kindrick is telling folks that he has heard from a reliable source that the preacher was being paid all along to keep his mouth shut, that the preacher visited them Parsons, and that he knew good and well what was going on."

"That's a lie," Mother gasped. "You said so, didn't you, Ben?"

Ben's voice rang across the field. "Of course, I said so. In fact, I threatened to shove his lies down his woolly throat."

Unused to such anger, I felt as if our world had come to

an end. Mother must have felt the same. I saw fire in her eyes and a storm on Bob's young face. Trembling and uncertain, I turned to Father, and the serenity on his countenance gave me hope. His blue eyes were as calm as a mill pond. Giving Ben an appreciative pat, he said, "I appreciate your loyalty, but fighting won't solve a thing. Thank God, none of the Parson money touched my hands. Paul Holmes took care of it, and he has a receipt, signed by the sheriff, showing that every cent was turned over to the law. It can be posted in the store, and I will see that it is."

Father's words soothed Uncle Ben. He took my hoe and hit a few licks on the cotton row. "The people of Holly Oak have got to pull together," he said. "According to Ed Corbatt, the school board is almost bankrupt. He says we will do well to get fifty dollars."

Father leaned on his hoe handle. "I know," he said. "And we have got to have a schoolhouse before September. The church can meet at our place, but the youngsters have got to have a place to learn."

The receipt was posted the next day. That hushed Fletcher up, and since he was the one bent on stirring up ill will, things quieted down. The first meeting was held to decide what was to be done about a new school. Ed Corbatt and Paul Holmes were to get whatever they could from the school board, and the rest would be raised by the people. Preacher Horton suggested a pie supper be held on the school ground. This meant that each woman and girl of the community would bake her favorite pie, wrap it in some lovely fashion, and then Preacher would auction it off to the highest bidder. There would be a prize for the prettiest girl and one for the ugliest man. Bids on either of these would cost a dime, and all proceeds would go into the school building fund. Father promised to visit some of the sawmills to see how much lumber they would donate.

He came home from the meeting confident now that the people were cooperating. Not once did he mention the disappointment he suffered, knowing his church plans must be tabled indefinitely. But the next day, when I was going after the cows, I came upon him, alone and in a state of prayer. Feeling like an intruder, I circled my father, and he never knew I was there. But I heard him pray, "Give me patience, O God, to labor on, knowing that in due time you will provide a church for that strip of land. In the meantime, give us a school, and if it is thy will, use this misfortune to win Jim Hagerton to the Lord."

Later that evening, Uncle Ben brought from the post office a letter addressed to Father from Grandpa Wilson. News of the school fire had reached Grandpa's ears, and he had written to offer a neighbor's assistance if Father was willing to work for it. He wrote: "Archie Jackson bought a stack of lumber back when peaches were selling good, planning to build another shed. Then the bottom fell out of prices, and the building materials have been laying there. I spoke to him about the fire, and he has offered to let you have the lumber, roofing, nails, in fact the whole batch, if you would be willing to use your team in the peach crop for a couple of weeks."

It didn't take Father long to make up his mind. It was a Monday evening, and we were all gathered in the living room when he read the letter. Turning to Ben, he said, "The crops are laid by. Think you can hold things down for a couple of weeks?"

I couldn't believe my ears. We hadn't visited our grandparents since we had come to Holly Oak a year and a half before.

"Sure. Go right ahead," Uncle Ben said. "Sounds like the best offer we have had so far."

I still couldn't believe it, but Father had made up his mind to go. To Mother he said, "Get our things together, including several dozen fruit jars. You might as well can some peaches while we are there." Then reaching for his cap, he headed for the door. "I'll ask Paul to conduct services the Sunday we are gone."

In a state of excitement, Bob and I helped Mother pack.

When Father returned, he told us we would leave before daylight the following morning.

Next morning we were up before the whippoorwill went to bed. We had breakfast by lamplight, and we were a mile down the road when Mother remembered her freshly washed fruit jars, still stacked on one end of the front porch. Father turned the horses around, and from the back end of the wagon, I noticed a streak of lightning in the west and a veil-like mist hovering over the valley below.

As I feared, before we could get the jars loaded, fat drops were splattering on my nose. By the time Father had driven the wagon into the shelter of the barn hallway, the landscape was blotted out in a downpour.

After a mad dash to the house, we children sat in the porch swing watching for some sign of clearing. But it wasn't until late afternoon that the sun peeked out and a multicolored rainbow arched the sky. How I longed to get back into the wagon and get on with the trip. But the roaring of the creek told us it was out of its banks, and all hope of making the trip that day was out of the question.

After an eternity in my child-world, night came, and the following morning dawned as blue as a robin's egg. In the early dawn the world smelled as fresh as a mountain stream. Once again we climbed into the wagon, and the horses clomped their way down the mountainside.

At the foot of the mountain we left our farm behind, and for the next four miles we rode through a wilderness of trees and hollows. Every turn of this houseless stretch reminded my brother and me of some story worth retelling. "Daddy," Bob said, "show us from here where you found the Indian carvings."

Father pointed up a narrow canyon to a solid gray stone, slanting downward at the head of a hollow. There Father and his young friend Jim had found stone carvings in the likeness of turkey feet, human footprints, dog tracks, and a couple of turtles. Sadness shadowed Father's eyes when he remembered his friend. "Jim found some arrowheads and other Indian relics not too far from there a few days before he was arrested," he said.

Knowing Father planned to stand by Jim and to do what he could to get his prison sentence shortened, Mother said, "You ought to drop Jim and Calvin a line, telling them about the job and that you will be visiting them when you get back."

Father nodded his head; then we were nearing a huckleberry thicket, and he changed the subject to happier things. "Ben tells me that he once picked a tub of berries in that patch," he said.

"Yeah, and did he tell you that he came close to stepping on a rattlesnake with eight buttons?" Bob asked.

"He told me," Father said, and to our surprise, he turned the horses off the road and drove them up an overgrown path. To Mother's questioning eyes, he said, "Ben used to farm here. He says there should be some peaches in the old orchard. I am craving fruit—think I will take a look."

He stopped the horses near a chimney where a house had once stood. While Mother and I waited, old Bell switched her tail, and a green horsefly darted from one hip to the other. Undisturbed, old Kit closed her eyes for a few winks of sleep. When the morning sun grew hot on our backs, Mother opened a big, black umbrella. "It's going to be a hot day," she said. "We shouldn't be wasting time." Just then, our men came through the thicket, and the day seemed full of delightful surprises, for both Father and Bob had a double handful of peaches.

A few miles on, houses began to appear. Some of the hill folk were taking advantage of the cool porch shade. Some of the women were bent over washboards, and often men were seen behind plows. But busy or not, we were greeted with an invitation to "pull over and sit a spell." But we hastened on to Martin Springs where we were refreshed with a cool drink and a box lunch. Here, someone had built a concrete square around a spring and had inserted a pipe; a continuous stream of water gurgled forth to refresh man and beast. With children in mind, some other thoughtful soul had cut slits in surrounding sweet gum trees, and Bob and I gathered a chew of pleasant tasting sweet gum (sweet rosin).

When we climbed back into the wagon, Mother opened a second umbrella for us children, and this time we welcomed the shade. But we did not have much farther to go until Redlick mountain gave way to a valley where acres and acres of orchards had been planted. Spring had been as gentle as a farmer's dream, with no late frost, and now, as we passed orchard after orchard, it seemed as though each tree was trying to outproduce the other. Some of the limbs were so heavy that they had been propped up to keep them from breaking.

At Ludwig we turned down a red clay lane, and Grandpa's house was seen against a backdrop of well-shaped fruit trees. With open arms we were greeted in that area of rolling hills and little blue streams.

During the two weeks of our visit, we children spent some of our happiest days. Always at Grandpa's heels, we worked for thirty-five cents a day. Alongside sweating men and women, we picked, defuzzed, and packed fruit, kissed scarlet by the uncomfortable sun.

Up and down the rows, two fruit-hungry kids feasted on overripes until the juice ran down our faces. But the work gave us ravenous appetites, so we still had room for Grandma's peach cobblers, smelling faintly of nutmeg and piled high with thick cream.

Though Mother and Grandma were not busy in the orchards, they were far from idle as the top of the barn clearly showed. It was lined with tray after tray of reddish peach halves, drying in the sun. Jars of fruit lined the kitchen wall, and peach preserves bubbled on the stove.

During the peach harvest, breakfast was eaten before sunrise. Dad and his team left for the neighboring Jackson orchard, and we children waded the dew with Grandpa. More than once he suggested we wait until the sun had dried the grass. But we didn't want to miss a thing. There was always something new going on, or the possibility of a story when we gathered around the water keg.

One afternoon I found a stray cat someone had dropped at the shed. While I was wondering how I might get it to the house without an adult being the wiser, Grandpa sat down on a crate beside me. He had come up so quietly that it was like having him come right out of nowhere. "Picking up a stray cat is bad luck," he said.

Determined that the boney little thing should be fed, I said, "How do you know?"

"How do I know?" he cried. "I know because I was once as young as you, and picking up strays brought me a good deal of bad luck as I recall." Removing his straw hat, Grandpa mopped a fringe of white hair back from his rosy brow. "Let me tell you about the cat my sister Meg and I found," he said. "It was one of them long-haired cats, white with eyes as blue as yonder sky. Can't imagine why anyone would have wanted to get rid of a cat like that. But someone did, and Meg and I found it. Knowing how Ma felt about another pet, we knew we shouldn't coax it, so we didn't. But at the same time, I must admit, we didn't discourage the critter either. Well, it followed us home from school. In our rush to convince Ma that we hadn't anything to do with it, we let the dog in the house. A fight broke out between the two animals, with so much ruckus Ma couldn't hear a word we said. She grabbed the broom and swished them both outside, but her new wallpaper had been torn and an antique mirror broken. My mother was a patient woman, but needless to say, Meg and I received a double portion of bad luck."

I enjoyed Grandpa's story, but I assumed it was his way of saying I should leave the cat at the shed. "If I can't take it, may I bring it something to eat from the house?" I asked.

His blue eyes grew merry and under a chuckle he said, "I didn't say you couldn't take it. I said it was bad luck, and it seems we are doomed to a certain portion anyway. As I recall, that cat sister Meg and I found turned out to be a mighty good mouser, and Ma came to like her by and by."

Carl Newton, a middle-aged worker, had brought a basket of peaches in while Grandpa was talking. Hearing the tail end of the conversation he said, "Then you fared better than I did, Mr. Wilson. I once mistook a sick buzzard for a turkey. When I brought it home from school, my mother gave me a bath in lye soap."

While we were laughing at Carl's bad luck, the sun dropped behind Stillwell Mountain, and Grandpa called "quittin' time."

Bob, busy in the trees, joined me for a ride home on horseback. When I climbed astride the harnessed back, Grandpa placed the cat in my lap, and we started homeward.

Midway across the pasture, we paused to allow the horses to drink from the creek. Charley, my mount, began to drink in loud, thirsty sips, and I could feel his swallowing muscles against my bare leg.

Grandpa rounded up the cows while we were refreshing the horses. When our horses began to spit, we edged them forward until the cool water covered the soles of our feet. Then we moved on like a caravan, with the cows falling in behind.

At the barn we were met by Grandma, holding a pail in each hand. Father came in from the Jackson orchard about this time, and he helped do the milking while Grandpa fed the teams.

When the chores were done, Mother had supper on the table. For the next thirty minutes we feasted on the products of our labors—corn on the cob, green beans, ham, and fresh churned butter.

After the dishes were put away, everyone moved to the front porch, hoping the house would cool before bedtime.

Soon a neighbor or two stopped by to discuss low peach prices, the weather, or the coming picnic. One evening, one of Father's old school teachers stopped by to see him. She said, "We heard about the fire. And some of the women have suggested a bakery goods booth at the picnic, with the proceeds going to your school."

Father thanked her, and since the gathering would be held the weekend we were in Ludwig, he said we would attend. I had never been to this sort of get-together, but listening to all the talk, I could hardly wait to go. Grandpa told me it was more fair than anything and that I would see some of the largest watermelons, the highest cakes, and some of the finest canned goods I was likely to see again.

He was right. When Saturday came, I found myself in front of booths where green beans were crisscrossed like rail fences in their jars. Tomatoes were canned whole, and peach pickles were packed in such a way they looked like freshly pulled peaches. Quilts in many patterns—Flower Garden, Jacob's Ladder, Wedding Ring, and many others—were hanging on lines, along with embroidery and lacy crochet items.

Well in advance, a table of great dimensions had been set up to receive potluck food that would be shared by all. Hawkers were shouting, "Get your ice cream and your lemonade here. Five cents a cone, just five cents a cone."

I wanted an ice cream cone so badly I could taste it, but a horse drawn merry-go-round claimed the two nickels I had been allotted.

After the evening feast around the great table, children were given free rides on the merry-go-round, while men competed in sack races, horseshoes, and weight-lifting contests.

The festivities continued until the sun dropped out of sight. Then lanterns strung around a platform were lighted. Married folks gathered on backless benches to visit and listen to the music that was yet to come. Fiddles were tuned, and at last a slender young man stepped to the center of the platform and began to call the "figures." Young people chose their partners, and the dancing began. Like many of the adults, Father did not approve of dancing. But he enjoyed the music, and he believed that everyone had a right to abide by his own conscience. So we stayed on far past my bedtime until at last I fell asleep with my head on Grandma's lap, my ears full of tapping feet keeping time to an Ozark ballad.

When the picnic was over, Miss Lula, as Father called his childhood teacher, brought six dollars to be contributed to the building fund. The next weekend Father loaded as much as he could of the lumber which he had worked for on our wagon and the rest on Grandpa's logging wagon. Mother and I climbed to the spring seat behind Bell and Kit. Grandpa, Father, and Bob got in the other wagon, and we started home.

6.
The
Building
of the
Church
and
School

According to Uncle Ben, a lot
of good things had happened while we were gone. "There
is a lot of lumber stacked on that school ground," he said.
"Paul contacted a number of sawmills in addition to the men
you spoke to, and it seems each has tried to outdo the other.
Just may be there will be some left over to start the church."
We were having supper while he talked, and the old man
looked up from the peach pie Mother had prepared specially
for him. He paused in his school-church talk to compliment
her cooking. "For some reason, I was getting a little tired
of my own vittles. Thank the Lord you are back," he said.
Then he went on with the community news. "A new family
moved into the Parson place."

"What sort of family?" Father asked.

"Mountain family, I would say. A middle-aged woman
and a young man passed here in a wagon, piled high with
household goods, followed by three goats, a cow, and a hound
dog named Drum."

I wondered how Uncle Ben knew the dog's name, and as
if he had read my thoughts, he said, "Every time that

bloomin' dog got out of sight that old lady would yell, 'Here Drum, here Drum,' until you could hear her all over the mountain. Even so, the strangest thing about the couple was the piano they was a-toten."

Father set the mashed potatoes down with a bang. "What sort of piano?" he asked.

"Looked like a baby grand," Uncle Ben said. "It was all polished, and the sun glistened on it like it was brand-new. I heard down at the store that the woman is widowed and the son, Charles Gilmore I think his name was, is a fine musician."

Father planned to call on the new people as soon as he could, but the next few days were taken up with surveying the building materials and taking a trip to the county seat in behalf of Jim Hagerton and Calvin Lee.

With the help of a sharp lawyer, the Parsons received a light sentence in the state of Arkansas, but they were sent back to Chicago to stand trial for bootlegging and murder.

Father, Paul, and Ed did all they could to help our two men, but Calvin and Jim were sentenced to Cumins State Prison. With time off for good behavior, they would serve a year.

During one of Father's visits to the jail, Jim said, "Preacher, I realize now that I had to come here before I could humble myself before God. I am truly sorry that I couldn't accept your God before all this happened, but my heart just wasn't ready."

In the presence of his mother and the indifferent Calvin, Jim gave his heart to Christ. With tears in his eyes he told Mrs. Hagerton, "I'll be a different man when I come home. I'll try to make up to you for all the sorrow and embarrassment I have caused."

When Father said good-bye, he asked the young men if there was anything he could do for them. Calvin shook his head, but Jim said, "Well, there is one thing, ask Sally to write to me."

For a stunned moment, Father's surprise must have been

written all over his face, for Jim hurried on to explain. "I have always admired her, and there was a time when we cared for each other. I couldn't behave, and she worried about being four years older. Finally, we called it quits. I am sure I never cross her mind. But there has never been anyone else for me. But Lord-a-mercy, I have got a nerve asking you to do this for me. Here I am in jail, and Sally is such a fine clean-cut sort of person. Forget it, friend. Maybe someday things will be different, and I can go to her a decent man."

But Father didn't forget. When he mentioned the request to Mother, she showed no surprise. Pausing at the ironing board, she said, "Sally once told me they had had a few dates and that Jim had considered himself in love with her. She told me in such a casual way I forgot all about it. But looking back it does seem strange that a lovely girl like Sally dates no one."

When Father gave Sally Jim's message, her dark eyes grew wishful. "So he hasn't forgotten," she said. She kept her eyes on the floor, and when her gaze flickered once to Father's face, he saw two large tears.

"You still care?" he asked.

When she spoke, there was a tremor in her voice.

"I care, but I am a coward," she said. "I am almost thirty, far too old to be carried away by the rash promises of a twenty-five-year-old jailbird. How can I be certain he has changed?" she pleaded.

As friend and pastor, Father had prayed for guidance before he came. But Jim's conversion was a personal matter, and if Sally insisted on a guarantee, he could give none. "I believe in Jim," the preacher said. "But more important, I believe in God and his power to transform. Love requires a great deal of faith regardless of who the person is. I realize you will need more in this case, and it is a decision you alone will have to make. But you will have my prayers and my support whichever path you choose."

When Father left Sally, he made his way to the sawmill

cabin to see what might be done for Millie and little Ruthie.

He found the door open, and what few belongings they had were gone. Pinned to the "fireboard" above the fireplace was a note. Millie had written:

Der Precher:
    I am goin' with my brother. I ken pick coton in the botom. I shor love you folks.
Millie L.

With the matter of Jim and Calvin settled, Father remembered the new family. When Mother and Dad went calling, they found the old house as bright as the August sunlight. The Parsons had put down floor coverings and papered over the newspapers. But it was Mrs. Gilmore's own special touch that made the place so livable. Curtains and spreads had matching handmade lace, and the windowsills were lined with all sorts of potted plants.

While Mother was admiring the handwork, her hostess busied herself with "lasses cake" and coffee. But she talked about Charles. That her son was the apple of Fannie Gilmore's eye was obvious, and little wonder. From a wall photograph, my parents could see the young man was a replica of his deceased father. Around the table while the three adults were enjoying the cake and coffee, Fannie told how Charles, Jr., had inherited all of his father's musical talent. Then there was a step on the front porch, and the visitors were introduced to a towering, dark-eyed young man.

At his mother's suggestion, he went to the piano and according to Father, "He played as softly as a waterfall rippling into a brook."

Seeing the pleasure on the faces of her guests, Fannie said proudly, "His father studied music in Kansas City. A sickly man, he came to the mountains for his health. He boarded with my folks, and I was barely seventeen when we fell in love." As Fannie talked, her amber eyes gave off a warmth which everyone could feel, and her tilted nose gave her a mischievous look. Running a hand over her ample middle, she said, "Believe it or not, when I met big Charles, I was a size nine, but I have always been strong as a horse. To look at my man, you would never have guessed he was as sick as he was, but he had TB and his health never improved. My love never had the chance for fame and honor like his son will have. He died when Charles, Jr., was ten, but he had taught the boy most of what he had learned at the conservatory. Just last week we got a letter from a big band in Saint Louis. They are going to audition my boy the next day after New Years. He is bound to get a contract, don't you think so?"

Charles had continued to play while his mother talked. But he paused now, and giving a modest wink in Fannie's direction, he said, "I gather you have noticed that Mother is my devoted fan. Unfortunately, her love makes her a lousy critic. But I do have hopes that I'll land something with this orchestra."

Father said he would practically guarantee it, and Mother had no doubts whatever. So the young man's fame spread fast throughout our community. Soon all sorts of gatherings were held at the Gilmore place where the added pleasure of Charles' baby grand could be enjoyed. Finally, the church was moved from our house to a spare room Fannie fixed up, and the piano brought husbands out of the shade into the preaching service, thus solving Father's problem of how to get the menfolk under the sound of the gospel.

Meanwhile, the building of the school was in full swing with every man giving a portion of his time to the project. And while newspaper accounts of the Parsons' bootlegging and the school burning had seemed like bad publicity for our community, they did bring about a great deal of good. Small offerings came from many different churches, saying, "It's time Holly Oak has a church building." Old desks, already well carved, and blackboards came from a school that was being dismantled. Offers for lumber came from different sources, and hammering and sawing filled the daylight hours. But with rain, harvesting of crops, and other problems, the building was not ready for school until mid-October. By then, the golden month had moved across the hills like a giant kaleidoscope changing green mountains to all the colors found on an artist palette. First, fingers of ivy twined along the gray rails of a crisscrossed fence turned to flame. Then scarlet tongues of sumac lapped against clay banks where sassafras grew and turned orange under nighttime's crisp blue sky. Hardwood seemed to be trying to outdo the sweet gums along school trails, and I noticed how lazily yellow butterflies fluttered, and crickets chirped their farewell songs in half-hearted notes.

Coming home from school, I enjoyed the last of the summer sun falling on yellow pears a few stunted trees had produced on our land. And late apples gleamed in the orchard like ruby gems. Hog apples lost their leaves and stood aflame with Christmas berries. Squirrels hustled about, laying in their winter store, and the smell of frost clung to the plants as farmers gathered their corn. Housewives gathered the last of the garden, lining window sills with peppers and tomatoes. Then just before Halloween a killing frost came, turning persimmons honey sweet, a feast for old man 'possum until he found his way to some hill man's table, all brown and ringed about with sweet potatoes.

In our new school we planned a Hallowe'en party, and children came dressed in homemade costumes. We ducked for apples, pulled taffy, which Miss Sally had prepared in advance, and finally, we were treated with apple cider.

Later at home, Uncle Ben gave us a ghost story or two. Looking back, I don't wonder that Mother sometimes cringed when our old friend began a tale. He told the unpolished truth as he had heard it, and if it wasn't "fitten" for a child's ears, that was just too bad.

So sitting around the kitchen fireplace, Bob, tall in his thirteenth year, and I, all legs in my eleventh, listened all ears when Uncle Ben began. "One of the ghosts that comes to my memory came into being when Jake Runnels shot himself. Some thought he did it because his old lady ran away with another man. I figured it was good riddance myself, and he seemed to have more sense to me. But I ain't sure why he did it, and that's neither here nor there. What counts in this story is the fact the old house stood empty for a number of years. Then some folks moved in, planning to farm the rich bottom land. They stayed exactly two nights. Both the man and woman claimed to have heard a walking, stomping ghost. According to them, the ghost walked right up the side of the outside wall, across the porch roof, and into the room where Runnels shot himself. There it walked 'til dawn, then came out the window, across the roof, and down the wall again.

"Finally Runnels' son who had been living out of state inherited the place. Laughing at the ghost story, he loaded up his wife and his furnishings, and he came there to live. The folks arrived after dark; and all tired out from travel, they threw a mattress on the floor of the fearful room and were falling into a peaceful sleep when steps tiptoed up the wall, across the roof, and for a heart-pounding moment the Runnels couple watched a hairy monster and two smaller ones come right through the window. Just when they were on the verge of a heart attack, they saw it was a nanny goat and her two kids.

"So the riddle of the Runnels' ghost was solved at last," Uncle Ben said, and then went on to explain, "Firewood had been left stacked almost to the top of the porch. Evidently, the goat and her kids had been climbing the woodpile and seeking shelter in the bedroom long enough to assume it belonged to her."

Uncle Ben bit off a chew of tobacco before he began his next tale. "I'll tell you one ghost story that is still a mystery," he said.

"For years, Harry Gross was a drinking, hell-raisin' citizen. One night on the way home from a party, he decided to spend the night in a deserted church. The leaning structure stood alone in a hollow, miles from anyone. Harry tied his horse to the front steps, went inside, and stretched himself out on a small platform in back of the pulpit. Sometime later, he was awakened by a snoring like he had never heard come from a human. Feeling a bit uneasy, he figured he had best be getting out of there. He felt around for his hat, and when he did so, his hand came to rest on a creature of huge dimensions; its body was covered with long, coarse hair. Harry forgot all about his hat. In his haste to escape, he upset the pulpit. It tumbled over onto the beast, and while the two were scrambling about, a full moon came from behind the clouds; and according to Harry, he had never seen anything like the creature he was wrestling with. Harry tore out of the building, with the thing behind him. It spooked Harry's horse, and the frightened man had to walk home alone. Hurrying along, he kept hearing steps behind him, and once a snort that could only mean the monster was trailing him. When Harry reached home, he loaded his gun and retraced his steps until he came head on with a large, dark form. Not daring to miss, he pulled both triggers of his double barrel. Just then, the moon peeked through the clouds once more, and Harry's stomach did a flip-flop. The creature he had shot smack-dab between the eyes was none other than his faithful horse. But mountain folks always reasoned that all was not in vain," Uncle Ben said. "For that experience cured Harry of his drinking bouts."

Uncle Ben's ghost stories could go on and on, and he knew an endless amount of things children should not do under pretense of bad luck. For instance:

A whistling girl like a crowing hen
Never comes to any good end.

Since a crowing hen usually went to the frying pan, I assumed the saying suggested something equally ominous for a whistling girl. But the idea never really stopped me. Neither did his admonition of bad luck when an umbrella was opened in the house. But there was one thing that could make the hair stand on the back of my neck. Every time a coon dog howled at the moon in a weird sort of way Uncle

Ben would add to the eeriness by saying, "Something bad is goin' to happen."

When the school was finished, work was begun on the church. A twenty-by-thirty-foot structure, it would have a small stage that would hold the pulpit and a ten-voice choir. When Nettie heard that Charles had volunteered to lead the music, she told Father that she had decided her old pump organ had been collecting dust long enough and that she was donating it to the church as soon as the building was completed. Father hoped the church would be ready for the Christmas pageant, and since Sally was in charge of the holiday entertainment, we children began our play practice at the school in late November. Meanwhile, everyone was getting ready for Thanksgiving. Uncle Ben said, "Thanksgiving marks the beginning of the cozy season." He meant that after the long hot days of planting, cultivating, harvesting, and canning, the holiday was the beginning of a long deserved rest.

Women of the hills knew that after Thanksgiving there would be time for sewing, quilting, and more visiting with neighbors. Men looked forward to hunting trips through woods abundant with nuts or through fields where golden corn shocks presented the perfect harvest picture.

But Thanksgiving meant something special to me that second year in the hills. There was going to be a reunion at Grandpa Wilson's house. That meant lots of good food, a visit with cousins, and a sort of magic that would not end until Christmas.

Days before, the windows of our school had been decorated with cutout Pilgrims, turkeys, and pumpkins.

When at last Miss Sally reached for the bell that would summon us to put away our books for four whole days, we were already on our feet. Other days she would have made us sit down again for a less hurried exit. But this was Thanksgiving, and being the preacher's daughter, I knew a secret. Sally was going to the state farm to visit Jim. They had been writing back and forth, and Jim had written that he felt called to preach the gospel when he came home. Sally and Father had talked about the possibility of seminary for Jim. Sally was hopeful, and I knew she was as anxious to be gone as we children were.

On the way home I noticed that the last purple leaf had fallen from the gum tree, and October's scarlet oaks had turned to brown. There was a frosty smell to the forest now, and in my excitement my feet skipped lightly over the crunchy, leafy carpet on the woods floor. I was remembering Lydia Maria Child's appropriate poem, learned only that day.

Over the river and through the woods,
To grandfather's house we go. . . .[1]

Before daylight the next morning old Bell and Kit were hitched to the wagon. A patchwork quilt was spread on the wagon bed. We children sat on it, and another was tucked snugly about us. Mother, Father, and Uncle Ben climbed to the spring seat.

Slowly the horses joggled the wagon forward. There were no worries about holiday accidents, and we were completely unmindful of the white mist our breaths made in the cold morning air. It was over the hills and through the creeks to Grandfather's house we went.

At the gate we were greeted by aunts, uncles, and a host of cousins. But Grandmother dared not leave the good things cooking on the big iron stove. She kissed our cold cheeks in the kitchen that served as a dining room as well.

The warm air was pungent with a combination of odors. A bit of hickory smoke lingered from Grandmother's having removed the stove cap to refuel. From the oven came the spicy fragrance of pumpkin pies, and the warming closet couldn't quite retain all of the smokey goodness of a baked ham.

When coats were removed, we children were shooed into the "front room" made cozy by a big open fireplace. Now Mother slipped into her apron, opened her basket, and set

[1] Lydia Maria Child, "Thanksgiving Day," *One Thousand Poems for Children*, selected and arranged by Elizabeth Hough Sechrist (Philadelphia: Macrae Smith Co., 1946), p. 184.

out her contribution to the Thanksgiving dinner. This included such homemade goodies as bread and butter pickles, wild grape jelly, kraut, and a jar of hominy. I couldn't help thinking how much my mother had learned from her neighbors during our two years in the hills.

Amid all of the joyous excitement with everyone talking at once, Grandfather came in clad in a heavy mackinaw with his arms full of firewood. When he stomped through the door, a blast of cold air swept through the room, and I felt the chill of it when I kissed his rough cheek. From his pockets he handed out apples taken from the straw in the barn, then settled back in his high-backed rocker. While we children played Grandpa's talking machine that played cylinder records, some of the men gathered around "the stand table" for a game of checkers.

In no time at all Grandmother was telling everyone to get washed up. Then we gathered around the big table made especially for the big Wilson family, and thanks was given for a bountiful year.

What a feast we enjoyed, and every dish was a fruit of our labor. One did not know whether to take some of Aunt Lena's baked hen pungent with dressing or sliced ham with "brown eye" gravy. Then there was Grandmother's hot, homemade bread and plenty of fresh butter. We had jellies of every sort and Aunt Bea's applesauce cake.

When dinner was over and the dishes put away, the women gathered at the fireplace to discuss children, news of old acquaintances, or the latest quilt pattern in *The Kansas City Star*.

While the women were talking in the house, the men were down at the barn, taking a look at Grandpa's hogs that were fat and ready to butcher. As I tagged along, I heard Uncle Ben say, "I am predicting a long, hard winter; the fuzzy caterpillar is showing more black than white.

"So it is," Grandpa agreed. "But I am not worried any. This is one winter I'll have a full smokehouse, apples in the barn, and canned goods aplenty."

By now, the sun was setting behind a purple mountain, and the wind had taken on a stronger bite. "We had better be hitching up the horses," Father told Uncle Ben.

Once more we were tucked into the wagon, along with tasty leftovers that would be eaten later by lamplight. Uncle Ben picked up the lines; we kids yelled our final goodbyes; and the horse, without being prodded, started homeward.

That Christmas was without a doubt the most wonderful holiday I have ever known. Maybe it was because it was the last Christmas of my childhood; maybe it was the thrill of seeing Father get his church or knowing that Bob would be going to live with Grandma Tate the next fall so he could attend Fort Smith junior high.

One thing I know for certain, from Thanksgiving on, there was an atmosphere of excitement and a feeling that something wonderful was about to happen. While Father was overseeing the church building, Mother was busy with nuts, cherries, preserves, and other good things that went into the making of a fruitcake. She zipped up warm nightgowns, aprons, and pillowcases, being careful to put things away before we children came home from school.

At the school the windows were decorated with Santas and crayon-colored Christmas trees. Names had been drawn, and Miss Sally said there would be candy and apples for everyone when the big tree went up at the church. In anticipation of that perfectly shaped cedar, a few minutes of each day were given to stringing hog-apples which the boys had gathered in the woods near the school. Oil lanterns hanging from the ceiling were polished and made festive with bunches of mistletoe. But one of the most exciting features was the daily play practice of the Christmas pageant. Every boy and girl would participate by song, verse, or lines. Parts were repeated so often each child came to know the entire program by heart, and yet it was thrilling. For we knew young and old would be willing to ride over unbelievable roads in an open wagon to see us perform.

Later at home alone in the quietness of the living room,

I could hear the fire "popping snow," the hum of the tea kettle in the kitchen, the ticking of the clock on the mantle, and Father chopping kindling outside. Soon he came inside, bringing a gust of frosty air and a black log for the fireplace. In it went, sending a host of sparks up the chimney, reminding me of Bethlehem stars and the reason we have Christmas.

As Christmas day drew near, we children hoped for snow. But the sky remained clear and unseasonably warm. Then on the night of the church pageant, as we joggled down the mountain behind Bell and Kit, the sky turned white and promising.

Amid the bustle of children dressing in a tiny room behind the choir, I slipped into my angel costume and then glanced out the window. Like a dream come true, I saw the ground was getting white, and the huge flakes drifting down showed no sign of letting up.

"Take your places," Miss Sally said. Then the curtain went up, and Charles at the pump organ hit the first chord of "Joy to the World."

As I raised my voice in praise, my eyes took in the great tree and all the upturned faces that had become so dear to me. There was Father, proud as punch on the front row. Beside him was Sally, ready to coach if we got bogged down. Her dark eyes had the sparkle of a woman in love. Behind her was Fletcher with his dingy beard, straining his ears to hear. Preacher and his brood filled the middle of the church. I saw Ed and Nettie, old Lidge, Paul and Deana, and across the aisle sat Ike and Nina Cocks. This was their first Christmas without Bill, and their faces lacked the joy reflected around the room. For an instant my own heart was saddened by the memory of that summer day. Then I remembered Father saying, "Time will heal," and I knew it would.

Mom: I just re-read this book and was amazed at how very creative Aunt Marie is. It's a very good book and I'm _so_ very proud to be related to the author. I know Grandma must have just puffed up with pride every time she got a chance to mention that Marie was her daughter. What a creative bunch of children God blessed her with. I recognize some of the storys & songs as things you had told me. I'm glad that Mrs. King had the idea of re-circulating this book. I love you!

Patti